Radiocarbon Dating

Radiocarbon Dating

By
Willard F. Libby

Phoenix Books

THE UNIVERSITY OF CHICAGO PRESS
CHICAGO & LONDON

PHOENIX SCIENCE SERIES

This book is also available in a clothbound edition from
THE UNIVERSITY OF CHICAGO PRESS

THE UNIVERSITY OF CHICAGO PRESS, CHICAGO & LONDON
The University of Toronto Press, Toronto 5, Canada

PREFACE TO THE FIRST EDITION

IT IS a real pleasure to acknowledge the invaluable contributions of my collaborators, Drs. E. C. Anderson and James R. Arnold, in the development of the dating method. Certainly nothing would have been done without them. Dr. A. V. Grosse and his collaborators at the Houdry Process Corporation concentrated the methane samples which first established the existence of radiocarbon in nature and laid a firm foundation for the program.

The Committee on Carbon 14 of the American Anthropological Association and the Geological Society of America, consisting of Frederick Johnson, chairman, Donald Collier, Richard Foster Flint, and Froelich Rainey, in selecting the samples for measurement, advising on priorities, and lending a friendly ear in troubled periods, have indeed earned our most heartfelt gratitude. We hope that the results of the research may in some small measure repay them for their efforts.

It is also a privilege to thank the Wenner-Gren Foundation for Anthropological Research, formerly The Viking Fund, Inc., and its director, Dr. Paul Fejos, for the financial support of this research with two grants totaling some $35,000 in the years 1948, 1949, and 1950. A small unexpended balance remains from these funds, which will be used over the years for occasional further measurements. This foundation, together with the University of Chicago, furnished the principal financial support for the entire research. We are very grateful indeed for this assistance.

We also are indebted to the Air Force (Wright-Patterson Air Force Base, Contract AF 33[038]–6492) for a contract for the development of low-level counting techniques during the year 1949, the results of which were put to immediate use in the radiocarbon dating research.

It is hoped that the present publication will contain the answers to most of the questions which will occur to an investigator constructing and operating equipment for the measurement of dates by the radiocarbon technique. It is realized, however, that certain important details may have been omitted, and we would be pleased to try to assist in the solution of any difficulties which other groups may encounter.

W. F. LIBBY

CHICAGO, ILLINOIS

PREFACE TO THE SECOND EDITION

THE improvements in the measurement technique developed since the first edition was published are described, and the hundreds of additional dates measured in our laboratory are included in the tabulation of radiocarbon dates in chapter vi. Chapter vii, "Reflections upon the Significance of Radiocarbon Dates," by Frederick Johnson, has been revised and expanded.

W. F. LIBBY

PREFACE TO THE SECOND EDITION

NOTES ADDED IN 1965 PRINTING

ADDENDUM TO CHAPTER I

No important new point of principle has appeared in the last ten years. However, considerable refinements have developed. It now appears that there is some evidence for a deviation in the period 4000–5000 B.P. (2000–3000 B.C.) in the direction of the radiocarbon dates being too young by perhaps 500 or 600 years for Egyptian samples at the time of the First Dynasty (4800 to 5000 B.P.). Good agreement generally has been found for the period back to about 4000 B.P. The question of the source of the disagreement in the fifth millennium remains to be resolved. If it is historical, the radiocarbon dating method will remain unaffected. If it is in the method itself, grave corrections might prove necessary for all dates older than 4000 years. (W. F. Libby, *Science* **140**, 278 [1963].)

ADDENDUM TO CHAPTER II

It appears that the specific activity of living matter now accurately measured to be close to 13.56 ± 0.07 disintegrations per minute per gram of carbon (J. Karlen, I. U. Olsson, P. Kalberg, and S. Kilicci, *Arkiv Geophysik* **4**, 465 [1964]) raises the question of the total makeup of the reservoir. In the work described in this chapter and in chapter i, the total reservoir was set at 8.3 grams of carbon per cm^2 corresponding to a decay rate of 1.9 ± 0.2 per cm^2 per second. The most recent estimates of the cosmic-ray production rate is 2.5 ± 5 per cm^2 per second (R. E. Lingenfelter, *Rev. Geophysics* **1**, 35 [1963]). The entire discrepancy, if real, could be removed by adding some 2–3 grams of carbon per cm^2 to the inventory, possibly as carbonate precipitation in the oceans. Owing to recent work on meteorites (M. Honda and J. R. Arnold, *Science* **143**, 203 [1964]), the evidence that the cosmic rays themselves have remained constant is stronger now than ten years ago, and the only other factor that might cause error is the earth's magnetic field, which acts to reduce the cosmic-ray intensity to about half the intensity a nonmagnetic earth would receive (W. Elsasser *et al.*, *Nature* **178**, 1226 [1956]). Some evidence exists for variation of the earth's total magnetic dipole (directional changes are of no importance to the problem because of the completeness of mixing) (T. Nagata *et al.*, *J. Geophys. Res.* **68**, 5277 [1963]).

ADDENDUM TO CHAPTER III

The half-life of radiocarbon now is accepted to be 5730 ± 40 years, but for reasons of consistency in reporting, radiocarbon dates are reported on the old value of 5570 years (H. Godwin, *Nature* **195**, 984 [1962]).

ADDENDUM TO CHAPTER IV

The black carbon method described in chapters iv and v now is obsolete. The present method uses pure carbon dioxide gas in a proportional counter as described in the last paragraphs of chapter iv.

ADDENDUM TO CHAPTER VI

Radiocarbon dates now are published in *Radiocarbon*, a supplement of the *American Journal of Science* (Yale University Press; Editors: E. S. Deevey, R. F. Flint, and I. Rouse). *Radiocarbon* now is in its seventh year (Vol. 6, 1964).

CONTENTS

CHAPTER I

PRINCIPLES*

T HE discovery of cosmic radiation by V. F. Hess in 1911 led
to repeated conjectures as to possible permanent effects this
radiation might have on the surface of the earth. The energy
received by the earth in the form of cosmic radiation is commensurate with that received as starlight. It is therefore really quite small
in terms of the solar energy. The specific energy, that is, the energy
per constituent particle, is very much higher than for any other type
of radiation, averaging several billions of electron volts (1 electron
volt is 1.6×10^{-12} ergs, which is the average energy of motion of a
gas molecule at 10,000° C.). It is conceivable, therefore, that the
cosmic radiation will alter the earth's atmosphere in detectable ways.

It was discovered shortly after the neutron itself had been discovered that neutrons were present in the higher layers of the atmosphere probably as secondary radiations produced by the primary
cosmic rays. Measurements by cosmic-ray physicists have clearly
established that the population in the atmosphere rises with altitude
to a maximum somewhat above 40,000 feet and then falls.[1] This
proves the secondary character of the radiation—that it is not incident on the earth from interstellar space but is a product of the im-
pact of the true primary radiation on the earth's atmosphere. The
decrease at the top of the atmosphere is due to the escape of some
of the neutrons formed from the earth. They are formed at high
velocity and will escape if they happen to fly off in an upward
direction when first produced. A corroborating point in this connection is the recent demonstration that the neutron is truly radioactive with a lifetime of about 12 minutes, which of course removes
any possibility of the neutrons having time to travel any consider-

---

* See Addendum to Chapter I, p. ix above.

1. H. M. Agnew, W. C. Bright, and Darol Froman, *Phys. Rev.*, **72**, 203 (1947)
(this paper contains references to many earlier measurements); J. A. Simpson, Jr.,
Phys. Rev., **73**, 1389 (1948); L. C. L. Yuan, *Phys. Rev.*, **74**, 504 (1948); L. C. L. Yuan
and R. Ladenburg, *Bull. Am. Phys. Soc.*, **23**, No. 2, 21 (1948); L. C. L. Yuan, *Phys.
Rev.*, **76**, 1267, 1268 (1949); L. C. L. Yuan, *Phys. Rev.*, **77**, 728 (1950).

able distance in interstellar space, though the trip from the sun could be made without complete decay to hydrogen.

Consideration of possible nuclear transmutations which the cosmic rays might effect leads one immediately to consider what the neutrons known to be produced by the cosmic rays might be expected to do to the earth's atmosphere. In the laboratory many studies have been made of the effects of neutrons of various energies on all the ordinary elements and especially on nitrogen and oxygen, the constituents of the air. In general, the results are that oxygen is extraordinarily inert but that nitrogen is reactive. It appears certain that, of the two nitrogen isotopes, N^{14}, of 99.62 per cent abundance, and N^{15}, of 0.038 per cent abundance, N^{14} is the more reactive. With neutrons of thermal velocity the reaction

$$N^{14} + n = C^{14} + H^1 \tag{1}$$

is dominant, the cross-section of the N^{14} atom for a room temperature thermal neutron being in the vicinity of 1.7×10^{-24} cm.^{2}, whereas the thermal neutron cross-section for reaction with O^{16} is of the order of 0.1 per cent of this. It is therefore quite certain that thermal neutrons introduced into ordinary air will react according to Equation (1) to form the radiocarbon isotope of mass 14 and half-life of 5568 ± 30 years.

The neutrons in the air being formed by the energetic cosmic rays possess energy themselves, probably of the order of 5–10 mev (million electron volts) on the average when first formed. After birth they then collide with the air molecules and lose their energy by collision, either elastic or inelastic, either reacting on one of these collisions and so being absorbed or finally attaining thermal energies where they are quite certain to be absorbed to form radiocarbon by Reaction (1). Laboratory studies of the effects of energetic neutrons on air again indicate that the nitrogen is the more reactive constituent. Reaction (1) is still dominant, though a second reaction,

$$N^{14} + n = B^{11} + He^4, \tag{2}$$

occurs.[2] The latter reaction becomes dominant at energies above 1 mev but even at the most favored energies attains cross-sections of only 10 per cent of that of nitrogen for thermal energies. Reac-

2. C. H. Johnson and H. H. Barschall, *Phys. Rev.*, **80**, 819 (1950).

tion (1), on the other hand, goes with considerable probability in the region of 0.4–1.6 mev.

A third type of reaction of high-energy neutrons with nitrogen,

$$N^{14} + n = C^{12} + H^3 ,\qquad(3)$$

has been reported in the laboratory.[3] The nature of the laboratory experiment was such that it was difficult to estimate the cross-section for the reaction, but the reported value was 10^{-26} cm.[2], to an accuracy of about a factor of 5. It is certain from the masses of the atoms involved in Reaction (3) that neutrons of not less than 4 mev are involved, since the reaction is endothermic to this extent. The hydrogen isotope in Reaction (3) is the radioactive hydrogen called tritium, of 12.46 years half-life, which decays to form the stable isotope of helium, He^3, which occurs in atmospheric helium in an abundance of 1.2×10^{-6} parts He^3 per ordinary helium in atmospheric air.[4] It is thought that this value is accurate to about 30 per cent. The abundance of He^3 in ordinary helium from terrestrial sources varies widely from undetectably small values in uranium ores, where an excessively large amount of He^4 is found, to the values of 12×10^{-6} parts for certain Canadian rocks. In general, however, the He^3 content of helium from the earth's crust is not over one-tenth as large as that of atmospheric helium. Since tritium produced by Reaction (3) lasts such a short time, one knows that any tritium produced by Reaction (3) will introduce an equivalent amount of He^3 into the earth's atmosphere, so that one possible effect of the cosmic-ray bombardment of the earth's atmosphere could be the introduction of He^3 into the atmospheric helium. It is seen that this may be the case, since it is observed that atmospheric helium is richer in He^3 than terrestrial helium.

Summarizing the three most probable reactions, only the first and third lead to radioactive isotopes. It is therefore to be expected that the neutrons produced by the cosmic radiation may produce these radioactive materials in the earth's atmosphere. After these points were made,[5] a search in nature for both radioactivities was insti-

3. R. Cornog and W. F. Libby, *Phys. Rev.*, **59**, 1046 (1941).

4. L. T. Aldrich and A. O. Nier, *Phys. Rev.*, **74**, 1590 (1948).

5. W. F. Libby, *Phys. Rev.*, **69**, 671 (1946).

tuted. Both have since been found[6] in amounts and concentrations corresponding roughly to those expected.

Therefore, we now have more confidence in the basic postulates made in the arguments outlined above—that the behavior of the cosmic-ray neutrons in the air is predictable from the observed behavior of laboratory neutrons on nitrogen and oxygen and that the possibility of the neutrons having higher energy than laboratory neutrons appears not to confuse the issue appreciably.

The prediction of the expected amounts of radiocarbon and tritium can be made only on the basis of some information about the relative probabilities of Reactions (1), (2), and (3). Reaction (1) is so much more probable, however, that it is clear that the yield of radiocarbon will be nearly equal to the total number of neutrons generated by the cosmic rays and retained on earth, a number which we shall call Q in units of number per square centimeter per second. The tritium yield, due to Reaction (3) only, is taken to be of the order of the ratio of these cross-sections, or about 1 per cent of Q. The latter will be considerably more uncertain than the yield of radiocarbon, since the cross-section for Reaction (3) is much more uncertain than that for Reaction (1) and more specifically than the dominance of Reaction (1). If we integrate the data for the neutron intensity as a function of altitude from sea-level to the top of the atmosphere, to obtain the total number of neutrons, Q, produced per square centimeter per second, and average this over the earth's surface according to the observed variation of neutron intensity with latitude,[7] we obtain a figure for $\bar{Q}$, the average number of neutrons generated per square centimeter of the earth's surface per second by the incidence of cosmic radiation. If we further assume that the cosmic-ray production of radiocarbon is an ancient phenomenon in terms of the 5600-year half-life of radiocarbon (i.e., the cosmic rays have remained at essentially their present intensity over the last 10,000 or 20,000 years), we can conclude that there is some place on earth enough radiocarbon to guarantee that its rate

6. E. C. Anderson, W. F. Libby, S. Weinhouse, A. F. Reid, A. D. Kirshenbaum, and A. V. Grosse, *Science*, **105**, 576 (1947); E. C. Anderson, W. F. Libby, S. Weinhouse, A. F. Reid, A. D. Kirshenbaum, and A. V. Grosse, *Phys. Rev.*, **72**, 931 (1947); A. V. Grosse, W. H. Johnston, R. L. Wolfgang, and W. F. Libby, *Science*, **113**, 1 (1951).

7. J. A. Simpson, Jr., *Phys. Rev.*, **73**, 1389 (1948); L. C. L. Yuan, *Phys. Rev.*, **76**, 1267, 1268 (1949).

of disintegration is just equal to its rate of formation. Evaluation of $\bar{Q}$ from the experimental data available gives 2.6 as a most likely value. Since the earth's surface has 5.1×10^{18} cm.^{2}, the radiocarbon inventory must be such that 1.3×10^{19} beta disintegrations occur per second.

$$C^{14} = \beta^- + N^{14+}. \tag{4}$$

Since laboratory measurement of the specific disintegration rate of radiocarbon[8] gives 1.6×10^{11} disintegrations per second per gram, dividing we obtain 8.1×10^7 grams, or 81 metric tons, as the predicted inventory for radiocarbon on earth. This is equivalent to 365 million curies (1 curie is that quantity of radioactivity which gives a disintegration rate of 3.7×10^{10} per second). Reasoning similarly, we predict a tritium inventory of about 3 million curies in nature.

The question remains as to where the radiocarbon will occur. A moment's thought answers this, however. We consider the problem of the ultimate fate of a carbon atom introduced into the air at a height of some 5 or 6 miles. It seems certain that within a few minutes or hours the carbon atom will have been burned to carbon dioxide molecule. It is true that there are points of interest to discuss in the question of the kinetics of combustion of atomic carbon in the air, and research is necessary to supply definite answers for the many questions which would arise in such a discussion. It seems probable, however, that the carbon will not long remain in any condition other than carbon dioxide. Postulating that this is so (i.e., the absorption of cosmic-ray neutrons by nitrogen of the air is equivalent to the production of radioactive carbon dioxide), we can proceed to an immediate answer to the question as to where natural radiocarbon should occur on earth. Radioactive carbon dioxide will certainly mix with considerable speed with the atmospheric carbon dioxide, and so we conclude that all atmospheric carbon dioxide is rendered radioactive by the cosmic radiation. Since plants live off the carbon dioxide, all plants will be radioactive; since the animals on earth live off the plants, all animals will be radioactive. Thus we conclude that all living things will be rendered radioactive by the cosmic radia-

8. A. G. Engelkemeir, W. H. Hamill, M. G. Inghram, and W. F. Libby, *Phys. Rev.*, **75**, 1825 (1949); W. M. Jones, *Phys. Rev.*, **76**, 885 (1949); W. W. Miller, R. Ballentine, W. Bernstein, L. Friedman, A. O. Nier, and R. D. Evans, *Phys. Rev.*, **77**, 714 (1950); A. G. Engelkemeir and W. F. Libby, *Rev. Sci. Inst.*, **21**, 550 (1950).

tion. In addition, there is another carbon reservoir for the natural radiocarbon, and this is the inorganic carbon in the sea present as dissolved carbon dioxide, bicarbonate and carbonate, for it is known that an exchange reaction occurs between carbon dioxide and dissolved bicarbonate and carbonate ions. The time for radioactive carbon dioxide in the air to distribute itself through this reservoir probably is not in excess of 500 years. This is the so-called "turnover" time for the life-cycle which has been widely discussed by geochemists. The estimates vary quite widely, but it does seem that this time can hardly exceed 1000 years. Since this is a time short as compared to the lifetime of radiocarbon, we conclude that any given radiocarbon atom will make the round trip several times in its lifetime, and we therefore predict that the distribution of radiocarbon throughout the reservoir will be quite uniform, there being little vertical or latitudinal or longitudinal gradients left. One has some cause to suspect that there might be variations in intensity over the earth's surface, for the reason that it is known that the cosmic-ray neutron component varies by a factor of about 3.5[9] between equatorial and polar regions, the intensity being greater in the polar regions.

As expected, however, on the basis of the probable brevity of the turn-over time as compared to the lifetime of radiocarbon, it has been found that the distribution is uniform. Materials have been selected from various points on the earth's surface and from various altitudes, and the specific radioactivity has been found to be identical within the error of measurement, which amounts to some 3–5 per cent.

In order to predict the specific radioactivity of living carbon, the amount of carbon in the exchange reservoir must be estimated. Careful consideration of the complex biochemical questions involved leads us to the numbers given in Table 1.

The dominance of the inorganic material dissolved in the sea is obvious from these numbers. This has the immediate consequence that variations in living conditions which will lead to variations in the amount of living matter on earth will not appreciably affect the total carbon in the reservoir. Or, conceivably, the only possible sig-

---

9. J. A. Simpson, Jr., *Phys. Rev.*, **73**, 1389 (1948); L. C. L. Yuan, *Phys. Rev.*, **76**, 1267, 1268 (1949).

nificant variations of the quantity of carbon in the reservoir must involve changes in the volume, the temperature, or the acidity (pH) of the oceans. This probably means that the reservoir has not changed significantly in the last few tens of thousands of years, though there is the point to consider of the effect of the glaciation on both the volume and the mean temperature of the oceans. If the numbers in Table 1 are correct, there are some 8.3 grams of carbon in exchange equilibrium with the atmospheric carbon dioxide for each square centimeter of the earth's surface, on the average, and, since there are some 2.6 C^{14} atoms formed per square centimeter per second, we must expect that these 8.3 grams of carbon will possess

TABLE 1

CARBON INVENTORY

Source	Amount (Gm/Cm²)
Ocean "carbonate"	7.25
Ocean, dissolved organic	0.59
Biosphere	0.33
Atmosphere	0.12
Total	8.3

a specific radioactivity of 2.6/8.3 disintegrations per second per gram, or 2.6 × 60/8.3 disintegrations per minute per gram. This number, 18.8, is to be compared with the experimentally observed value of 16.1 ± 0.5.[10] The agreement seems to be sufficiently within the experimental errors involved, so that we have reason for confidence in the theoretical picture set forth above.

The agreement between these two numbers bears on another point of real importance—the constancy in intensity of the cosmic radiation over the past several thousand years. If one were to imagine that the cosmic radiation had been turned off until a short while ago, the enormous amount of radiocarbon necessary to the equilibrium state would not have been manufactured and the specific radioactivity of living matter would be much less than the rate of production calculated from the neutron intensity. Or, conversely, if one were to imagine that the intensity had been much higher in the past until very recently, the specific radioactivity would greatly exceed that

10. E. C. Anderson, Ph.D. thesis, University of Chicago (1949); E. C. Anderson and W. F. Libby, *Phys. Rev.*, **81**, 64 (1951).

calculated from the observed neutron intensity. Since 5568 ± 30 years will be required to bring the inventory halfway to any new equilibrium state demanded by the change in cosmic-ray intensity, we find some evidence in the agreement between these numbers that the cosmic-ray intensity has remained essentially constant for the last 5000–10,000 years. This does not mean that it could not exhibit hourly, daily, or even annual fluctuations. It does mean, however, that the intensity averaged over 1000 years or so has not changed. There is the slight possibility that an approximately compensating change in the carbon inventory has occurred, but for the reasons mentioned above the buffering action of the great reservoir in the sea makes this very remote.

A further point of interest in connection with the inventory and the observed specific assay is that the carbon isotopes apparently are fractionated in being incorporated into the biosphere from the inorganic world. This effect was discovered some time ago[11] for the isotope C^{13}, which has a mean abundance of 1.1 per cent in ordinary carbon. It was found that the ratio of the abundance of C^{13} in inorganic carbon to that in biological carbon is 1.025. On the basis of this, one would expect a value of 1.05 for the analogous ratio for C^{14}, radiocarbon. Since the mass spectrographic measurements of the C^{13} abundance are quite accurate and the theory on which one calculates the 1.05 ratio from the observed 1.03 ratio for C^{13} is quite rigorous, we are inclined to multiply our assay of biological material by 1.05 rather than to take the mean value of the small number of measurements we have made on inorganic carbon. The mean of the biological assay is 15.3 ± 0.1. Multiplying by 1.05, we obtain 16.1 for inorganic carbon; then, averaging according to the weight factors given in Table 1, we derive the average 16.0 for the carbon inventory as a whole. One must remember, however, that wood or other biological material will present an assay of 15.3 and that modern seashell will present an assay of 16.1.

If the cosmic radiation has remained at its present intensity for 20,000 or 30,000 years, and if the carbon reservoir has not changed appreciably in this time, then there exists at the present time a com-

11. A. O. Nier and E. A. Gulbranson, *J. Am. Chem. Soc.*, **61**, 697 (1939); B. F. Murphy and A. O. Nier, *Phys. Rev.*, **59**, 771 (1941); H. Craig, *Geochim. et Cosmochim. Acta*, **3**, 53–92 (1953); H. Craig, *J. Geol.*, **62**, 115 (1954).

plete balance between the rate of disintegration of radiocarbon atoms and the rate of assimilation of new radiocarbon atoms for all material in the life-cycle. For example, a tree, or any other living organism, is in a state of equilibrium between the cosmic radiation and the natural rate of disintegration of radiocarbon so long as it is alive. In other words, during the lifetime the radiocarbon assimilated from food will just balance the radiocarbon disintegrating in the tissues. When death occurs, however, the assimilation process is abruptly halted, and only the disintegration process remains.

It has been known for many years that the rate of disintegration of radioactive bodies is extraordinarily immutable, being independent of the nature of the chemical compound in which the radioactive body resides and of the temperature, pressure, and other physical characteristics of its environment. The reason for this is that the transformation is a nuclear phenomenon involving energies very much larger than those corresponding to the chemical bonds and to the various physical influences to which matter might conceivably be subjected. Therefore, we conclude that the rate of disappearance of radioactivity following death corresponds to the exponential decay law for radiocarbon as represented by the solid curve in Figure 1, in which the world-wide assay of 15.3 for biological materials corresponds to zero time, and the predicted specific radioactivities for various times thereafter are given by the curve. The equation for the curve is

$$I = 15.3 \exp\left(-0.693 \frac{t}{5568}\right) \tag{5}$$

or

$$I = 15.3 \; 2^{(-t/5568)}, \tag{5'}$$

in which t is the age of the organic material in years, age being defined as the time elapsed since death occurred. The experimental points shown in Figure 1 are the observed assays for various samples of known age, discussed later. In so far as the points fit the curve, we have reason to believe that the method is sound and gives the correct ages. The errors indicated on the experimental points are standard deviations, and it appears that the results are favorable as judged statistically.

It is obvious that we must be careful, in selecting samples, to choose materials that contain the original carbon atoms present at the time death occurred. In other words, samples must not have been preserved with organic materials containing carbon of age different from that of the sample. Care must also be taken that chemical changes have not led to replacement of the carbon atoms. In a gen-

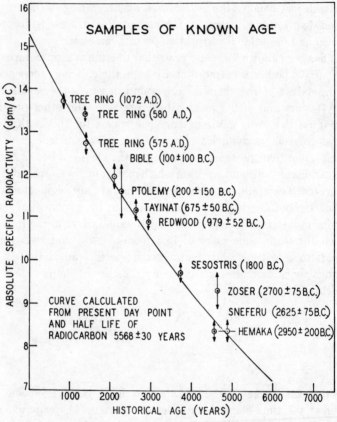

Fig. 1.—Predicted versus observed radioactivities of samples of known age

eral way, organic materials consisting mainly of large molecules, such as cellulose and charcoal, are favored. An example of questionable material is shell, for it is quite conceivable that shell which is powdery and chalky in appearance has had its carbonate atoms replaced.

It has recently been shown[12] that a New England lake whose bed was entirely ancient limestone and which was fed mainly by water leached through ancient limestone contained carbonate, bicarbonate, and CO_2 whose radiocarbon content was only 77 ± 2 per cent of the value for the carbon in modern wood. Also it was shown that in this particular lake the living material had specific activities below that of modern wood in the normal biosphere but not quite so low as the carbonate, bicarbonate, and CO_2 dissolved in the lake water. This experience cautions us that materials grown under such conditions must not be used for radiocarbon dating. Material that is likely to be supported in its growth, in any significant part, by carbon from limestone is, of course, useless.

12. E. S. Deevey, Jr., M. S. Gross, G. E. Hutchinson, and H. L. Kraybill, *Proc. Nat. Acad. Sci.*, **40**, 285 (1954).

CHAPTER II

WORLD-WIDE DISTRIBUTION
OF RADIOCARBON *

FUNDAMENTAL to the radiocarbon dating method is the question of the contemporary assay of the exchange reservoir for radiocarbon and the uniformity over the earth's surface of this assay.[1] Organic material, principally wood, was collected from widely scattered points over the earth's surface, and measurements of the specific radioactivity were made. One group of samples was concentrated near the geomagnetic equator, where the neutron flux is at a minimum; another in high latitudes, where the neutron flux is at a maximum. The variation in neutron intensity with latitude, as observed by Simpson at 30,000 feet, is presented in Figure 2.[2] Some consideration was given to the archeological importance of the region with the thought that, if no uniformity were demonstrated, these data might be utilized in age measurements where the original assay would vary from region to region. Fortunately, this has not proved to be necessary. Owing to the known extreme variation of neutron intensity with altitude, shown in Figure 3, in which the data of Yuan and Ladenburg taken at Princeton, New Jersey,[3] are given, two samples from high altitudes were measured. It might be suspected that the specific radioactivity would be higher at higher altitudes. However, the height of the timber line was of course very small indeed compared with the 30,000-foot altitude at which the principal radiocarbon production occurs.

The experimental results are given in Tables 2 and 3, in which the type of sample, the donor, the geomagnetic latitude, and the

---

* See Addendum to Chapter II, p. ix above.

1. The material on this subject has been taken largely from the doctoral thesis of E. C. Anderson, presented to the Division of Physical Sciences, University of Chicago, in partial fulfilment of the requirements for the Ph.D. degree. Cf. also *Ann. Rev. Nuc. Sci.*, **2**, 63 (1953).

2. *Ibid.*

3. *Phys. Rev.*, **74**, 504 (1948); **76**, 1267, 1268 (1949); **77**, 728 (1950); *Bull. Am. Phys. Soc.*, **23**, No. 2, 21 (1948).

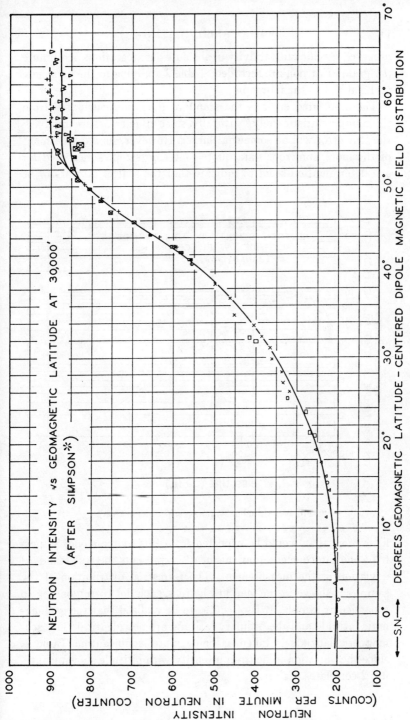

FIG. 2.—Latitudinal variation of cosmic-ray neutron intensity. (After J. A. Simpson, Jr., *Phys. Rev.*, 73, 1389 [1948])

observed specific radioactivity in absolute disintegrations per minute per gram of carbon are recorded, Table 2 applying to the biosphere and Table 3 to the inorganic.

The associated error is the standard deviation calculated from the counter statistics only. Naturally, since other errors are involved, the true error will be somewhat larger. However, similar treatment of the more numerous data quoted later on samples measured for age determination seem to indicate that the scatter appears to be

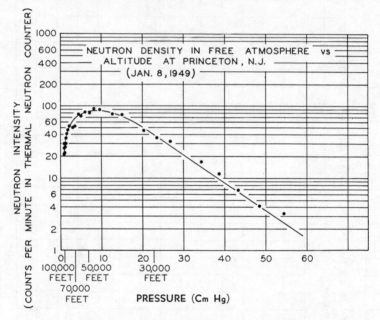

FIG. 3.—Altitudinal variation of neutron intensity

little more than would be expected from this source alone. So perhaps one can conclude that this nearly represents the true standard deviation of the measurement. The terrestrial distribution of the samples is shown in the map in Figure 4, each dot corresponding to a particular sample. It is of course to be realized that the geomagnetic latitude and the ordinary latitude are not identical. The geomagnetic latitude is taken as being more significant in Table 2, since the variation in neutron intensity with latitude shown in Figure 2 correlates with it.

TABLE 2

ACTIVITY OF TERRESTRIAL BIOSPHERE SAMPLES

Source	Geomagnetic Latitude	Absolute Specific Activity (Dpm/Gm)
White spruce, Yukon (Frederick Johnson)............	60° N.	14.84±0.30
Norwegian spruce, Sweden (Donald Collier, Chicago Natural History Museum)..........................	55° N.	15.37±0.54
Elm wood, Chicago (author).....................	53° N.	14.72±0.54
Fraximus excelsior, Switzerland (Donald Collier).......	49° N.	15.16±0.30
Honeysuckle leaves, Oak Ridge, Tennessee (C. H. Perry, Clinton Laboratory).............................	47° N.	14.60±0.30
Pine twigs and needles (12,000-ft. alt.), Mount Wheeler, New Mexico (Robert Fryxell).....................	44° N.	15.82±0.47
North African briar (John Hudson Moore, Inc.).......	40° N.	14.47±0.44
Oak, Sherafut, Palestine (Donald Collier).............	34° N.	15.19±0.40
Unidentified wood, Teheran, Iran (M. Hessaby).......	28° N.	15.57±0.34
Fraximus mandshurica, Japan (Donald Collier).........	26° N.	14.84±0.30
Unidentified wood, Panama (John Simpson)..........	20° N.	15.94±0.51
Chlorophora excelsa, Liberia (Donald Collier)...........	11° N.	15.08±0.34
Sterculia excelsa, Copacabana, Bolivia (9000-ft. alt.) (Donald Collier)...................................	1° N.	15.47±0.50
Ironwood, Majuro, Marshall Islands (Donald Collier)..	0°	14.53±0.60
Unidentified wood, Ceylon (Donald Collier)...........	2° S.	15.29±0.67
Beech wood ('Nothafagus), Tiera del Fuego (Junius Bird).......................................	45° S.	15.37±0.49
Eucalyptus, New South Wales, Australia (Donald Collier)	45° S.	16.31±0.43
Seal oil from seal meat from Antarctic (Byrd Expedition through H. J. Deason)..........................	65° S.	15.69±0.30
Average..	....	15.3 ±0.1*

* Error of calibration of counter raises error on absolute assay to 0.5.

TABLE 3

ACTIVITY OF CONTEMPORANEOUS SHELL SAMPLES

Source	Assay*
Four seashells from Lower California†	15.3±0.2
Six clam shells from New York† .,,.........	16.9±0.3
Bikini coral (Halimeda debris)‡	16.9±0.3
Clam shells from Aleutians§...................	13.3±0.5
Eleven mollusk shells from North America, ranging from Texas, California, and Florida to New England‖.........................	15.8±0.2
(Excluding two high values at 17.8 and 17.2...	15.4±0.2
Munex shell from Florida.....................	17.1±0.5
Fresh ocean sediment from Bermuda...........	17.4±0.5
Oyster from Chesapeake Bay.................	15.1±0.5

* All the analyses quoted from other laboratories are reduced by assuming that the modern wood assay is in perfect agreement with the average value deduced from the data in Table 2.

† H. Suess, *Science*, **120**, 467 (1954).

‡ J. L. Kulp, H. W. Feely, and L. E. Tryon, *Science*, **114**, 565 (1951).

§ J. L. Kulp, L. E. Tryon, W. R. Eckelman, and W. E. Snell, *Science*, **116**, 409 (1952).

‖ M. Blau, E. S. Deevey, Jr., and M. S. Gross, *Science*, **118**, 1 (1953).

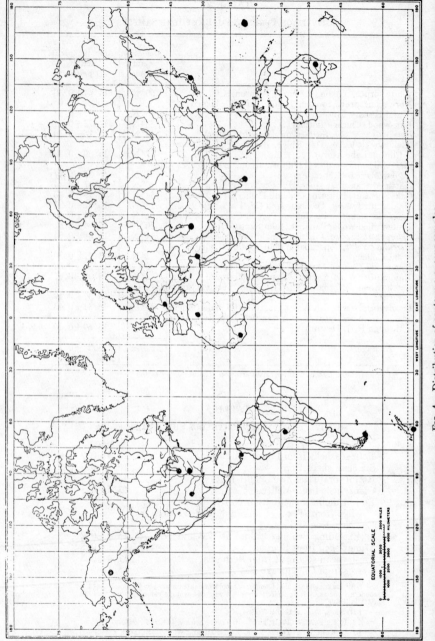

Fig. 4.—Distribution of contemporaneous samples.

The average specific activity of all the biosphere samples is found[4] to be 15.3 ± 0.5 absolute disintegrations per minute per gram. The data seem to show no scatter appreciably larger than the expected statistical fluctuations, indicating that the samples involved would indeed have specific activities identical within the error of measurement. The data presented in Table 3 for shell reveal that shell carbon is probably more radioactive than organic matter. This difference is to be expected, since it has been shown[5] that fractionation of the stable isotopes of carbon, C^{12} and C^{13}, occurs in these systems. The ratio of the C^{14} content of carbonate to that of organic material would be expected to be 1.05, since the careful work on C^{13} has shown a factor of 1.025.[6] The difference between this factor 1.05 and the one found in the data given in Table 3 may not be outside the experimental area. But one has the suspicion from examining the data in Table 3 that factors are operating which we do not understand clearly. It has been suggested[7] that upwelling of deep ocean waters which are somewhat deficient in C^{14}, apparently because of slightly imperfect mixing in the greatest depths of the ocean, may cause seashells growing in these regions of upwelling waters to be deficient in C^{14}. This would perhaps apply to the clam shells from the Aleution Islands. Since the accuracy of the estimation of the fractionation factor from the accurate C^{13} data[8] is better than the precision of our measurements of the shell activity, we take the observed value per shell to be 16.1, derived by multiplication of the mean of the organic specific activity by 1.05. It seems that a further investigation of the fractionation factor would be worth while and that further measurement of contemporaneous shell samples is definitely desirable.

The estimation of the amount of carbon in exchange with the atmospheric carbon dioxide is a difficult task. It is, however, necessary to the striking of a balance between the observed specific ac-

4. Earlier publications have given 12.5 for this number. The counters have been recalibrated for absolute efficiency since then, and the new value is derived from the old one by correction for the more accurately determined efficiency.

5. A. O. Nier and E. A. Gulbranson, *J. Am. Chem. Soc.*, **61**, 697 (1939); B. F. Murphy and A. O. Nier, *Phys. Rev.*, **59**, 771 (1941).

6. H. Craig, *J. Geol.*, **62**, 115 (1954).

7. J. L. Kulp, H. W. Feely, and L. E. Tryon, *Science*, **114**, 565 (1951).

8. A. O. Nier and E. A. Gulbranson, *J. Am. Chem. Soc.*, **61** (1939); B. F. Murphy and A. O. Nier, *Phys. Rev.*, **59**, 771 (1941); H. Craig, *J. Geol.*, **62**, 115 (1954).

tivity and the cosmic radiation intensity. The results have been given in Table 1.

The carbon in the exchange reservoir is obviously of three principal origins; namely, that dissolved in the oceans, the carbon of living organisms, and atmospheric carbon dioxide itself. We shall find that the latter two are so small as to be nearly negligible in comparison with dissolved material in the sea, principally carbonate and bicarbonate. Let us consider first the amount of carbon dissolved in the oceans as some species of carbonic acid. This amount can be calculated from a knowledge of two factors: the alkalinity and the pH of the ocean water. The alkalinity is the excess of positive ions over the anions of strong acids. This difference must be made up by the ionization of weak acids in order to preserve electrical neutrality. Since carbonic acid is the principal weak acid in the ocean, the situation is fairly simple. The total amount of dissolved carbon is not uniquely determined by the alkalinity alone, because of its variable equivalent nature due to the possibility of its existence in the neutral, monobasic, and dibasic forms: H_2CO_3, HCO_3^-, and CO_3^{--}. The ratio of the amounts in these forms must therefore be specified, and this ratio is, of course, determined by the pH. The necessary equations are

$$\frac{(H^+) \cdot (HCO_3^-)}{(H_2CO_3)} = K_1 \tag{6}$$

$$\frac{(H^+) \cdot (CO_3^{--})}{(HCO^-)} = K_2 \tag{7}$$

$$A = (HCO_3^-) + 2\,(CO_3^{--}) \tag{8}$$

$$S = (H_2CO_3) + (HCO_3^-) + (CO_3^{--}), \tag{9}$$

where A is the alkalinity due to carbonic acid, and S is the total amount of carbon present in the forms indicated. These equations can be combined to give

$$S = \frac{A}{1 + \dfrac{2K_2}{(H^+)}} \Big[\frac{(H^+)}{K_1} + \frac{K_2}{(H^+)} + 1 \Big]. \tag{10}$$

We must now consider the values to be adopted for the four constants in this equation; namely, the alkalinity, the hydrogen-ion concentration, and the two ionization constants of carbonic acid.

The average value of the alkalinity of the ocean seems to be well established as a result of numerous measurements by many investigators and has a value of 2.43 milliequivalents per liter.[9] The alkalinity is due almost exclusively to carbonate and bicarbonate, the amounts of phosphorus, arsenic, silicon, and other elements capable of forming weak acids being completely negligible. A slight correction can be made for the amounts of boron known to be present. Using only the first ionization constant of boric acid and taking the pH of the ocean as 8.0, we find the alkalinity due to boron to be 0.06 milliequivalents per liter.[10] The alkalinity due to carbon is therefore 2.37 milliequivalents per liter.

The variation in pH throughout the ocean is surprisingly small, and the average value is about 8.0[11] The small amount of variation found throughout the greater portion of the water map is graphically illustrated by the north-south section of the Atlantic Ocean given by Sverdrup *et al.* as taken from Wattenberg.[12] It is clear that over the major portion of the ocean the variation is only 0.1 pH unit.

It is of interest to compare the observed pH of ocean water with that calculated assuming complete equilibrium with the carbon dioxide of the atmosphere. The deep water which constitutes by far the largest fraction of ocean water is formed at high latitudes by the cooling of water of high salinity. Therefore we will assume Arctic conditions for the equilibration. For the apparent ionization constants of carbonic acid we will use experimental values which will be discussed below. These are $K_1' = 8.3 \times 10^{-7}$, and $K_2' = 6.3 \times 10^{-10}$, and are applicable to water of chlorinity 19.0 per mil at a temperature of $4°$ C. We will assume an alkalinity of 2.37 milliequivalents per liter and a partial pressure of CO_2 in the polar air of 0.23 mm. of mercury.[13] For the solubility of CO_2 in sea water we will use the data given by Sverdrup *et al.*[14] The result of this calculation is a pH of 8.10 for the water while at the surface. On sinking to the average

9. H. U. Sverdrup, M. W. Johnson, and R. H. Fleming, *The Oceans* (New York: Prentice-Hall, 1946), p. 208.

10. *Ibid.*, p. 199.

11. *Ibid.*, p. 208.

12. *Ibid.*, p. 210, Fig. 43.

13. K. Buch, *Acta Acad. Aboensis, Math. et Physica*, 11, No. 12 (1939).

14. *Op. cit.*, p. 191.

depth of the oceans (3800 meters), the pH will change to 8.01 as a result of changes of K_1' and K_2' with pressure. These results are in very satisfactory agreement with the observed pH of the deep ocean, namely, 8.0.

Because of the high ionic strength of sea water, namely, 0.9 molal, and the lack of knowledge of the activity coefficients of the species involved, it is necessary to use apparent ionization constants rather than thermodynamic constants for carbonic acid. Fortunately the values of K_1' and K_2' have been carefully investigated by a number of investigators[15] as a function of pH, salinity, temperature, and pressure in both natural and artificial sea water. In general, the agreement among the several investigators is excellent, and the results appear to be very reliable.

The relations which were found for the normal range of composition of sea water are

$$pK_1' = 6.47 - 0.100 \text{ (Cl)}^{1/3} \tag{11}$$

at $20°$ C. with a temperature coefficient of -0.008 per $°$ C. and a pressure coefficient of -4.8×10^{-5} per meter of depth; and

$$pK_2 = 10.35 - 0.498 \text{ (Cl)}^{1/3} \tag{12}$$

(where pK is the negative logarithm, base 10) at $20°$ C. with a temperature coefficient of -0.011 per $°$ C. and a pressure coefficient of -1.8×10^{-5} per meter. Taking (Cl) as 1.95 per cent, the temperature to be $4°$ C., and a depth of 3800 meters (the mean depth of the ocean), we find that for average ocean water

$$K_1' = 1.26 \times 10^{-6} \tag{13}$$

$$K_2' = 7.41 \times 10^{-10} \tag{14}$$

From Equation (10) it is possible to calculate the errors which will be introduced into the value of the total carbon by errors in K_1', K_2', and pH. If we substitute the following numerical values in Equation (10), $K_1' = 1.20 \times 10^{-6}$, $K_2' = 7.41 \times 10^{-10}$, and $(H^+) = 10^{-8}$, we find

$$S = \frac{A}{1 + 0.148} (0.0082 + 0.074 + 1). \tag{15}$$

15. E. G. Moberg, D. M. Greenberg, R. Revelle, and E. C. Allen, *Bull. Scripps Inst. Oceanogr.*, Univ. California, Tech. Ser., **3**, 231 (1934); K. Buch, *Acta Acad. Aboensis, Math. et Physica*, **11**, No. 5 (1938); Sverdrup et al., op. cit., p. 250.

It is clear that K_1' has a completely negligible effect on S, since it contributes only 0.8 per cent to the last term.

Dropping K_1' and expanding Equation (10) in terms of powers of $[K_2'/(H^+)]$, and dropping higher powers than the first, we have, to a good approximation,

$$S = A \left(1 - \frac{K_2'}{(H^+)}\right) = A \,(1 - 0.074). \qquad (16)$$

The entire effect of K_2' is only 7.4 per cent. If for the possible error in K_2' we allow the amount of the full range between K_2 and K_2', we will estimate the possible error in S from this source as 7 per cent.

The error introduced in the value of S by an error in pH can be calculated by differentiating Equation (10) with respect to $-\log (H^+)$. In this way we find

$$\frac{dS}{d\,(\text{pH})} = -3.42 \times 10^{-9} \, \frac{(H^+)}{(H^+ + 2K_2')^2}. \qquad (17)$$

At pH 8 a change of one pH unit gives a change of 0.36 in S, or 16 per cent. If we assume that the uncertainty in the exact average pH of the ocean is 0.5 pH unit, we place an error of 8 per cent on the amount of dissolved carbonate.

The variations in alkalinity which have been observed in water from various sources by different investigators amount to about 4 per cent. We may take this as a measure of the uncertainty in A. Combining the errors from K_2', pH, and A, by the square root of the sum-of-squares method, we place an uncertainty of 11 per cent on the value of S.

Using the values of $K_1' = 1.26 \times 10^{-6}$, $K_2' = 7.41 \times 10^{-10}$, pH = 8.0, and $A = 2.37$, the solution of Equation (10) gives for S a value of 26.2 milligrams of carbon per kilogram of sea water, or 7.25 gm/cm^2 of earth's surface. This corresponds to a total mass of 3.7×10^{19} grams of carbon. In addition to the dissolved inorganic carbon, there is found in solution in the ocean a considerably smaller amount of organic carbon (not living). The best value for this appears to be about 2 mg. per liter, according to Sverdrup et al.[16] This corresponds to 0.59 gram of carbon per square centimeter of the earth's surface.

The amount of carbon in living material is difficult to estimate and appears to have been grossly overestimated by some writers in the

16. *Op. cit.*, p. 250.

past. We will base our estimate on the rate of fixation of carbon by photosynthesis, a quantity which appears to be fairly well established.[17] Fortunately it can be shown that biosphere carbon is small compared with ocean carbonate, and therefore an error in the estimation of it will not be of great importance to our use of this quantity.

The total rate of fixation of carbon by land plants has been investigated by Schroeder,[18] who concluded that the average annual fixation by this source is 1.63×10^{16} grams, or 3.2 mg/cm² of the earth's surface. Riley[19] made an investigation of the fixation by ocean plankton and arrived at a figure of 30.5 mg/cm² of earth's surface for the average annual rate. Rabinowitch[20] estimates that, on the basis of the solar energy flux, reflection losses, and photosynthetic efficiency, not more than 60 mg/cm² of earth's surface could be fixed annually, indicating that Riley's figures could not be too low by any large factor. On the other hand, it appears that the estimate of Vernadsky,[21] who gives 2000 mg/cm² for the carbon content of the biosphere, with renewal several times a year, is energetically impossible. We will use the sum of the values given by Schroeder and by Riley as the total annual rate of fixation of carbon; namely, 33 mg/cm² of the earth's surface.

The total amount of carbon contained in the biosphere at any time will be given by the fixation rate times the average length of time a given carbon atom spends in the biosphere, if a steady state exists. An estimation of this time is somewhat easier than might appear on first glance, since 90 per cent of the fixation is by ocean plankton, which are minute organisms of very short life. Furthermore, even the carbon contained in longer-lived organisms does not in general have a time of residence in the organism equal to the life of the organism but rather less because the material of the organism is replaced a number of times during its lifetime. A maximum value for the average time the carbon atom spends in the biosphere seems to

17. E. Rabinowitch, *Photosynthesis and Related Processes* (New York: Inter-Science Publishers, Inc., 1945), chap. i.

18. G. Schroeder, *Naturwiss.*, **7**, 8, 96 (1919).

19. G. A. Riley, *Bull. Bingham Oceanogr. Coll.*, **1**, 1 (1941), quoted by Rabinowitch, *op. cit.*, p. 6.

20. *Op. cit.*, p. 6.

21. W. J. Vernadsky, *Geochemie in ausgewählten Kapiteln* (Leipzig: Akademische Verlagsgesellschaft, 1930).

be a few years. Since carbon in the biosphere is such a small fraction of the total exchange reservoir, a more exact treatment appears unnecessary. Taking 10 years for the average carbon life, our calculated biosphere inventory will be 0.33 gm/cm^2 of the earth's surface, which will prove to be only some 4 per cent of the total in the exchange reservoir, as has been shown in Table 1.

We may check this estimate against measurements which have been made of the ratio of living matter to dissolved organic carbon in the ocean. A number of such measurements have been made by several observers,[22] and the ratio of dissolved to living matter has been determined to vary between 300:1 and 2:1. The low figures are found only in relatively small areas near shore where there is intense biological activity. The larger ratio, which was established for the deep water of the open ocean, was probably considerably nearer the average for the ocean as a whole. The estimates which we have chosen for these two quantities give a ratio of 2:1, again indicating that we have not underestimated the amount of carbon in the biosphere.

The most likely way of appreciably increasing the holdup of the biosphere is by the assumption that a considerable portion of this material spends many years in slow decay as humus or ocean sediments before it is recirculated. The available evidence for the ocean sediments seems to be that the major part of the dead material dissolves during the settling process and that little of it ever reaches the ocean floor.[23] This makes it unlikely that this factor could increase appreciably the importance of biosphere carbon to the size of the exchange reservoir.

The amount of carbon dioxide in the atmosphere has been determined by several people. The values are: Buch,[24] 0.12 (polar) to 0.13 (tropical and continental); Paneth,[25] 0.12; and Vernadsky,[26] 0.12. We will use 0.12 gm/cm^2 of the earth's surface for the amount of carbon in atmospheric carbon dioxide. This is equivalent to CO$_2$

22. Sverdrup *et al.*, *op. cit.*, p. 250.

23. *Ibid.*, p. 1012.

24. K. Buch *Acta Acad. Aboensis, Math. et Physica*, 11, No. 12 (1939).

25. F. Paneth, quoted by G. P. Kuiper, *The Atmospheres of the Earth and Planets* (Chicago: University of Chicago Press, 1949), p. 1.

26. *Op. cit.*

partial pressure of 0.21 mm. of mercury, or a concentration of 0.028 per cent.

In addition to the dilution of cosmic radiocarbon by the carbon of the exchange reservoir, some is being removed constantly by incorporation in sedimentary rocks as they form. This rate of loss of radiocarbon will be estimated. The rates of deposition of calcium carbonate in the sea are not at all well established. Various estimates can be made on the basis of the total amount of calcium carbonate that has been deposited, the bicarbonate contents of rivers emptying into the sea, and the direct observation of the rate of formation of ocean sediments. For example, Brown[27] has calculated the following inventory of carbon in the sedimentary rocks: in shale, 5.45×10^{21} grams; in sandstone, 0.20×10^{21} grams; and in limestone, 3.67×10^{21} grams—a total of 9.3×10^{21} grams of carbon. If we assume uniform deposition over a 2-billion-year period, we have a yearly loss rate of 5×10^{12} grams, which would remove only 6 grams of the 9800 grams of radiocarbon produced each year. This may be low because recycling may be important, and the other methods give somewhat higher figures; but it seems likely that the total removal by formation of sedimentary deposits is probably less than about 3 per cent.

We may consider now the question as to whether or not the various portions of the exchange reservoir are sufficiently well mixed so that they are completely efficient in the dilution process. The uniform distribution of radiocarbon throughout the reservoir will result only if the various mixing processes are complete in a time short compared with the average life of radiocarbon (8033 years; the average life is longer than the half-life by $1/\ln 2$). From the estimated photosynthetic fixation rate given above and the total material in the exchange reservoir, it can be calculated that a time of the order of 250 years would suffice to turn over all the carbon through the biosphere. This insures that the thin layer of the reservoir at the surface of the earth and of the ocean will be well mixed. The main question is whether or not the depths of the ocean and the upper reaches of the atmosphere are mixed.

Considering the latter first, we note that the radiocarbon is produced at great heights (Fig. 3), the neutron intensity reaching a

27. H. S. Brown, private communication.

maximum at about 40,000 feet and falling off considerably by 70,000 feet. At this altitude the air pressure is 3.5 mm. of mercury. Excellent and rapid mixing is well established in the troposphere, the adiabatic portion of the atmosphere in which most weather phenomena occur. In the meteorological "standard atmosphere" the tropopause, or boundary between the adiabatic troposphere and the isothermal stratosphere, is assumed to be[28] at 10.8 km. (36,000 feet). However, the height of the tropopause varies considerably with the season and with latitude, reaching 18 km. (58,000 feet) in the winter at 40° N. latitude, while in summer it may be found at 16 km. (52,000 feet) as far north as 60° N. geomagnetic latitude.[29] Thus the tropopause is actually above the altitude of maximum neutron intensity some of the time each year. Even the isothermal stratosphere is not without vertical mixing.[30]

The situation with regard to oceanic mixing is much less obvious. Very little indeed is known about the quantitative rates of convective mixing of the deep ocean basins. Diffusive mixing is of course so extremely slow as to be out of the question.

From studies made of the circulation of the Atlantic Ocean[31] a very rough estimate of the mixing time can be made. These figures indicate that the rate of flow southward between South America and Africa at the equator is about 6×10^6 cubic meters per second at 3000 meters depth. This flow has been identified with North Atlantic Deep Water produced in the Arctic regions, and much of it reaches the Antarctic to replace water subsiding at the Antarctic Convergence. The situation is greatly complicated by the presence of some six water masses interacting in an involved circulatory pattern, but we may take this figure to represent the gross exchange of water between the North and South Atlantic at great depths. The shallower water is mixed more rapidly by local complexities in the circulation pattern, and the surface water is characterized by well-developed patterns of rapid currents. The Antarctic Bottom Water, which fills the deepest parts of most of the Atlantic, moves

28. H. R. Byers, *General Meteorology* (New York: McGraw-Hill Book Co., 1944), p. 171.

29. C.-G. Rossby, in *The Atmospheres of the Earth and Planets*, ed. G. P. Kuiper (Chicago: University of Chicago Press, 1949), p. 21.

30. L. Spitzer, Jr., *ibid.*, p. 221.

31. Sverdrup *et al.*, *op. cit.*, pp. 629 and 747 ff.

slowly north below the southward current and is presumably returned to the Antarctic by gradual mixing with the North Atlantic Deep Water. The rate of the return is not known, but the northward flow at the equator is estimated at 1×10^6 cubic meters per second.

Taking the volume of the Atlantic Ocean as 3.24×10^{17} cubic meters, we find the calculated time of circulating the entire ocean through the entire Deep Water current to be 1700 years. About 18 per cent of the Atlantic is below 4000 meters. If this water has a circulation rate of 1×10^6 cubic meters per second, the time required to circulate it is 1800 years. Less is known about the Pacific circulation, but it is thought to be somewhat slower than that of the Atlantic.

For isolated seas for which the annual inflow and outflow are known, it is possible to calculate a renewal time. Some of the figures so obtained are: Mediterranean, 80 years; Arctic Mediterranean, 165 years; and Black Sea, 2500 years. The volume of such seas makes their importance in a general mixing process small, but the figures given are an indication of the order of magnitude of the time scale involved.

A further argument in favor of complete mixing of the ocean basins may be based on the following considerations: It is known that heat is being liberated from the earth's crust at the rate of about 30 calories per square centimeter per year.[32] Presumably the evolution of heat from the bottom of the sea is of a similar magnitude, as indeed recent measurements by Revelle and associates in the deep Pacific have shown.[33] Owing to this heat evolution, one might expect regions of temperature inversion to develop near the ocean bottom, especially in areas of poor circulation. To transfer this amount of heat by molecular conduction would require a thermal gradient of 8×10^{-4} °C. per centimeter, assuming the conductivity of water to be 0.0013. If a layer 1000 meters thick at the bottom were cooled only by molecular conduction, a temperature difference of 80° C. would be required. Naturally, turbulent eddy circulation patterns would be set up at much lower gradients, and a more effective

32. E. C. Bullard, *Nature*, **156**, 35 (1945).

33. Roger Revelle and associates, private communication. They find 38 calories per square centimeter per year.

mechanism of eddy conduction would operate to remove the heat. Such eddy circulation would be equally efficacious in the transfer of dissolved carbonate, and a very efficient method of maintaining the radiocarbon equilibrium would arise. It can be calculated, for example, that a temperature gradient of 1.6×10^{-6} ° C. per centimeter would require a coefficient of eddy conduction some five hundred times the molecular coefficient for the transfer of the postulated amount of heat. This is quite small as eddy coefficients go, since they often range up to 10^8 or more times the molecular coefficients. Such an eddy circulation operating at a depth below 4000 meters can be shown to be adequate to mix the ocean depths sufficiently so that the assay of radiocarbon at 6000 meters would be 90 per cent of normal with an integrated effect of only 1.4 per cent on the value of the specific activity.

Few cases of temperature inversion in the deep ocean have been established. The inversion gradient shown in the above calculation is that observed in the Mindanao Trench[34] and is almost exactly equal to the gradient which would be produced by adiabatic compression; that is, there is no density inversion, the density of the water being constant with depth. However, the smaller the thermal gradient, the larger the coefficient of eddy conduction required to transport the heat. Without specifying the nature or source of the circulation, we merely point out that if 30 calories per square centimeter per year are being evolved from the ocean floor, a certain minimum rate of circulation must exist in order to prevent the development of large thermal gradients. The above arguments are of course qualitative, since turbulent eddy circulation is not amenable to calculation. However, if the assumption of the specified heat evolution is correct, the absence of appreciable thermal inversions near the ocean bottom would seem to indicate that the mixing is very good indeed on our time scale.

It has not been possible to obtain samples of dissolved carbon from the very deep ocean, so that experimental evidence on the mixing time is not at hand. It would appear that measurements of this kind might be of considerable oceanographic interest and might shed some light on the problem of circulation in the deep basins. It is to be noted that collection of the deep water must be done with care, so

34. Sverdrup et al., op. cit., p. 739.

that particulate material in transit from the top to the bottom and probably in equilibrium with the biosphere will not be taken as part of the sample proper. It seems likely that matter falling through the deep water would not come into exchange equilibrium with dissolved material.

We arrive finally, therefore, at the numbers given in Table 1 and a total figure of 8.3 gm/cm² of the earth's surface for the carbon in the exchange reservoir. The uncertainty in this value for the total carbon in the reservoir we place at about 15 per cent, most of this error being in the estimated uncertainty in the value for ocean carbonate, since it is the largest single item in the reservoir. It is interesting to compare our numbers with a similar set given by Rubey.[35] Dr. Rubey's numbers are 7.85 gm/cm² for the total, consisting of 6.95 for ocean and fresh water, 0.125 for the atmosphere, and 0.775 for living organisms and undecayed organic matter.

We shall turn now to the question of the present production rate of radiocarbon as judged from the observed neutron intensity in the atmosphere, assuming essentially quantitative conversion of atmospheric neutrons to radiocarbon by Equation (1). As stated previously and shown in Figure 3,[36] the neutron intensity increases with altitude from sea-level up to about 40,000 feet in an exponential fashion, with a half-thickness of about 1 meter of water equivalent. Above 40,000 feet a maximum is reached, followed by a rapid decrease, indicating very low intensity at the very top of the atmosphere, in agreement with the principle that the neutrons are secondary in origin, and escape from the earth in part. In addition to the altitude dependence, the neutron intensity shows a strong dependence on geomagnetic latitude (Fig. 2),[37] the intensity at high latitudes being about four times that at the geomagnetic equator.

The measurements on neutron intensity which we use for our calculations of total intensity have been on the thermal component as defined by cadmium absorption for a boron detector. We shall take this to mean that that fraction of the neutron spectrum lying

35. W. W. Rubey, "Geological Evidence Regarding the Source of the Earth's Hydrosphere and Atmosphere," *Science*, 112, 20 (1950); and autumn, 1950, meeting of the National Academy of Sciences.

36. L. C. L. Yuan, *Phys. Rev.*, 74, 504 (1948); 76, 1267, 1268 (1949); 77, 728 (1950); L. C. L. Yuan and R. Ladenburg, *Bull. Am. Phys. Soc.*, 23, No. 2, 21 (1948).

37. E. C. Anderson, Ph.D. thesis, University of Chicago (1949).

below 0.4 ev has been measured, and, in order to calculate the total number of neutrons per square centimeter, Q, and its world-wide average, $\bar{Q}$, we must determine theoretically the probable ratio of the total intensity to the thermal intensity. Bethe, Korff, and Placzek[38] and Placzek[39] have considered the problem in detail. Following them and using the later data of Melkonian[40] together with the data in the Massachusetts Institute of Technology volume,[41] we shall assume that in the range 0.4 ev to 0.5 mev the total cross-section in units of 10^{-24} cm.^{2} for air is given by

$$\sigma_t = 8.56 + (0.266/E^{1/2}),\tag{18}$$

and that the capture cross-section is given by

$$\sigma_c = 0.266/E^{1/2}.\tag{19}$$

The expression for the ratio of the total number of neutrons generated to the number which reach the thermal range is e^y, where y is given by

$$y = \frac{1}{0.124} \int_{0.4}^{5 \times 10^5} \sigma_c dE / \sigma_t E,\tag{20}$$

where the number 0.124 is the fractional energy loss in elastic collision with the average air atom, the bond strength being neglected. Integration and substitution give 0.79 for the integral and the calculated ratio of total production to thermal population of 2.20. It is clear, however, that one must consider the effect of the very strong bonds in the nitrogen and oxygen molecules on the cooling process. Study of the analogous problem of the effect of binding on the neutron elastic and inelastic cross-sections for hydrogen[42] leads us to expect that no large error is made in neglecting the binding for cooling down to the cadmium cut-off of 0.4 ev, which is 1.5 vibrational quanta for the average air molecule.

It is necessary to make a correction for the absorption above 0.5 mev. It has been shown by Barschall and Battat,[43] Johnson and

38. H. A. Bethe, S. A. Korff, and G. Placzek, *Phys. Rev.*, **57**, 573 (1940).

39. G. Placzek, *Phys. Rev.*, **69**, 423 (1946).

40. E. Melkonian, *Phys. Rev.*, **76**, 1750 (1949).

41. *Science and Engineering of Nuclear Power* (Cambridge, Mass.: Addison-Wesley Press, 1947), **1**, 408–11.

42. H. A. Bethe, *Rev. Mod. Phys.*, **9**, 122–27 (1937).

43. H. H. Barschall and M. E. Battat, *Phys. Rev.*, **70**, 245 (1946).

Barschall,[44] and others,[45] that resonance production of radiocarbon occurs in this range at cross-sections rising to a maximum of 0.1×10^{-24} cm.^{2} and falling to about 0.01×10^{-24} cm.^{2} in the range 0.5 mev to 2.0 mev. To obtain a probable upper limit for the capture contribution in this high-energy range, we assume that only elastic scattering occurs and that an average capture cross-section of 0.035×10^{-24} cm.^{2} applies throughout the high-energy interval. This gives an additional contribution of 7 per cent to the ratio of total to thermal neutron population. The corrected ratio is 2.36. The value of Q is now to be obtained at any given latitude by integrating the observed intensity under the intensity versus altitude curve (e.g., Fig. 3) and multiplying this observed intensity by the number 2.36. For this purpose we choose the data of Yuan and Ladenburg,[46] Figure 3, obtained at Princeton, New Jersey, which give 1.9 as the number of slow cosmic-ray neutrons absorbed per second per square centimeter of earth's surface at that latitude. Using Simpson's data[47] (Fig. 2) for the variation of Q with latitude, and integrating over the surface of the earth, we find for the average thermal flux 1.1 thermal cosmic-ray neutrons per square centimeter per second. Finally, multiplying by the ratio of total production to thermal neutron population, we obtain 2.6 as the most likely value for Q, the average total production of cosmic-ray neutrons per square centimeter of earth's surface per second. Ladenburg[48] and Kouts and Yuan[49] have calculated the $\bar{Q}$ by somewhat different methods and arrived at 2.4. It seems likely that their calculation is more reliable than the one above.

If the figure 2.4 for the average total production of cosmic-ray neutrons per square centimeter of earth's surface per second, $\bar{Q}$, is correct, and this intensity has remained constant over the last several half-lives of radiocarbon, we can calculate an expected specific activity for the carbon in the exchange reservoir of $(2.4 \times 60)/8.3$, or 17.3 disintegrations per minute per gram of carbon. This

44. C. H. Johnson and H. H. Barschall, *Phys. Rev.*, **80**, 819 (1950).

45. *Science and Engineering of Nuclear Power*, **1**, 408-11.

46. L. C. L. Yuan and R. Ladenburg, *Bull. Am. Phys. Soc.*, **23**, No. 2, 21 (1948).

47. E. C. Anderson, Ph.D. thesis, University of Chicago (1949); *Ann. Rev. Nuc. Sci.*, **2**, 63 (1953).

48. R. Ladenburg, *Phys. Rev.*, **86**, 128 (1952).

49. H. J. Kouts and L. C. L. Yuan, *Phys. Rev.*, **86**, 128 (1952).

is to be compared with the observed mean value (Table 2) of 16.0 ± 0.5. Both of these numbers are for the average carbon in the inventory and are very close to the number expected for carbonate carbon, which is some 6 per cent higher in its radiocarbon content than biological carbon. The agreement between these two values is gratifying and suggests that no major factors contributing to the situation have been overlooked, although it does seem possible that the agreement may be due in some part to cancellation of errors.

The possibility that the amount of carbon in the exchange reservoir has altered appreciably in the last 10,000 or 20,000 years turns almost entirely on the question as to whether the glacial epoch, which as we will see later appears to reach into this period, could have affected the volume and the mean temperatures of the oceans appreciably. Antevs,[50] Daly,[51] and Flint[52] give 90, 85, and 102 meters, respectively, for the lowering of the seas below the present level during the last Ice Age. This is to be compared with the mean depth of 3800 meters, so we may expect a decrease in the volume of the sea by about 5 per cent during this period, the actual magnitude depending on the extent of the continental shelf in shallow regions in this sea. This effect in itself would lead to an increase in the specific activity of carbon formed during the glacial epoch by about this same percentage. In addition, there is the question of the mean temperature of the oceans and whether this has varied appreciably. An increase in mean temperature would act to increase the carbon in the reservoir, and a decrease in mean temperature would decrease the inventory. Bearing in mind that both of these effects will be unimportant unless the altered conditions last for a time of the order of magnitude of the mean life of radiocarbon (8033 ± 50 years), we find it difficult at this stage to make correction for these effects. It does seem possible, however, that the certain decrease in volume and the possible slight decrease in temperature might raise the specific activity of carbon in the exchange reservoir during the glacial maximum by 5 or 10 per cent, causing an error

50. *Am. Geog. Soc., Res. Ser.*, No. 17, pp. 74–82 (1928).

51. *Changing World of the Ice Age* (New Haven: Yale University Press, 1934), p. 46.

52. *Glacial Geology and the Pleistocene Epoch* (New York: John Wiley & Sons, 1947), p. 435.

in the direction of making glacial material appear somewhat too young. We can estimate from the decay equation

$$I = I_0 e^{-t/\tau} , \tag{21}$$

in which I_0 is the original specific activity and τ is the mean life, that the error in the age will be given by

$$\Delta t = \tau \sqrt{\left(\frac{\Delta I}{I}\right)^2 + \left(\frac{\Delta I_0}{I_0}\right)^2} , \tag{22}$$

in which ΔI is the error in the determination of the specific activity of the ancient material and ΔI_0 is the error made in assuming that I_0 has the modern value of 15.3 for organic matter or 16.2 for shell and inorganic material. From this we see that a 10 per cent error in I_0 would make our glacial ages too young by some 800 years. As further information becomes available on the chronology of the recent ice ages, it should be possible to make a more accurate correction for this effect. It is to be hoped that Professor Urey's determination of prehistoric temperatures by the O^{18} content of fossil shell[53] will give quantitative information on the mean temperature of the oceans in recent glacial times. With such data one then can calculate the expected change in the principal item in the inventory, the inorganic carbon in the sea. The data available at present suggest that the temperature correction will not be large, though it must be borne in mind and considered to be a source of uncertainty.

It seems quite likely that the amount of living matter on earth will not seriously affect the specific activity, for the reason that it constitutes such a small fraction of the total inventory in the reservoir and probably has always held this minor position. The situation would appear to be similar for the other two items in the inventory, the dissolved organic material in the ocean and atmospheric carbon dioxide.

The question of the constancy of the cosmic radiation intensity is much more difficult to answer. One feels that it is not unlikely that the intensity has remained constant in the sense we demand;

53. H. C. Urey, *Science*, **108**, 489 (1948); J. M. McCrea, *J. Chem. Phys.*, **18**, 849 (1950); S. Epstein, R. Buchsbaum, H. A. Lowenstam, and H. C. Urey, "The Carbonate-Water Isotopic Temperature Scale," *Bull. Geol. Soc. Am.*, **62**, 417 (1951); H. C. Urey, H. A. Lowenstam, S. Epstein, and C. R. McKinney, "Measurement of Paleotemperatures and Temperatures of the Upper Cretaceous of England, Denmark and the Southeastern United States," *Bull. Geol. Soc. Am.*, **62**, 399 (1951).

namely, variations in the average intensity over periods commensurate with the lifetime of radiocarbon, since it appears to be a phenomenon originating in the cosmos and therefore probably tied to a time scale similar to that controlling the intensity of solar radiation. However, it is not obvious a priori that this is true, and we must admit the possibility of variations having occurred. About the only sources of information on this point discovered so far have been the agreement between the specific activity of the present-day inventory and the observed present rate of production and observation that ancient materials of historically known age appear to exhibit the radiocarbon content calculated on the assumption that their original assay was identical with that of the modern reservoir. We have seen how uncertain the experimental information on the present rate of production is and are therefore forced to conclude that agreement between this rate and the radioactivity of modern material, which of course reflects the production rate as of some 8000 years ago—since the carbon atoms now found in modern wood, for example, are 8000 years old on an average—is not a very firm proof of the constancy and intensity of the cosmic radiation. It does, however, agree with this postulate. The rather satisfactory agreement between the predicted and observed radiocarbon contents of organic materials of historically known age (Fig. 1) is somewhat more reassuring. Taking the oldest materials with an age of some 4000 years, we observe their radiocarbon content, which was of course due to an average production some 8000 years previous to their existence, or some 12,000 years before the present, appears within the experimental error to have been the same as at present. This of course assumes that the size of the reservoir has not changed simultaneously and in a compensating manner. However, for the reasons given above we do not think that a significant factor of this sort is very likely. Considering the matter empirically, we are apparently justified in saying that, whatever the reasons, the specific activity of living matter has not changed significantly in historic times, and the problem resolves itself into consideration of possible variations restricted to the prehistoric period encompassed by the radiocarbon dating method.

CHAPTER III
HALF-LIFE OF RADIOCARBON[*]

THE half-life of radiocarbon has been measured several times. Table 4 gives the results obtained, together with the method of measurement. It is clear at a glance that the early measurements in which the amount of radiocarbon in the sample being measured was based on estimated bombardment yield gave high values. The later measurements based on mass spectrometric assays divide into three groups, according to the method of measurement: (a) counting of solid barium carbonate with thin window counters; (b) gas counting with the carbon disulfide–carbon dioxide mixture described by Miller and Brown;[1] and (c) gas counting with CO_2 either as a small additive to the standard argon–alcohol counter gas or as CO_2-methane mixture in the proportional counter. Miller et al.[2] have given evidence that the latter group is more nearly correct. It seems on first principles that the point of 100 per cent efficiency for ionizing radiations is most definitely settled in the case of standard argon–alcohol gas mixtures and probably in the case of the proportional counting technique. The first group, using the solid barium carbonate technique, seems to be subject to more errors in that more serious corrections for scattering and absorption are involved. The second group presents answers which are not clear in their significance, and the discussion of Miller et al.[3] casts considerable doubt on the validity of the results obtained by this technique. Therefore, in seeking the most probable value for the half-life of radiocarbon, we select the three values determined by the gas-counting technique with ordinary gas mixtures. They are 5580 ± 45;[4] $5589 \pm$

[*] See Addendum to Chapter III, p. x above.

1. W. W. Miller, Science, 105, 123 (1947); S. C. Brown and W. W. Miller, Rev. Sci. Inst., 18, 496 (1947).

2. W. W. Miller, R. Ballentine, W. Bernstein, L. Friedman, A. O. Nier, and R. D. Evans, Phys. Rev., 77, 714 (1950).

3. Ibid.

4. A. G. Engelkemeir, W. H. Hamill, M. G. Inghram, and W. F. Libby, Phys. Rev., 75, 1825 (1949); A. G. Engelkemeir and W. F. Libby, Rev. Sci. Inst., 21, 550 (1950).

TABLE 4

Summary of the Previously Published Values
for the Half-Life of Radiocarbon

Half-Life (Years)	Method for Isotopic Composition of Sample	Method for Radioactivity of Sample	Reference*
$10^3 - 10^5$	Estimated bombardment yield	Solid carbonate counting: $CaCO_3$ in screen-wall counter	[1]
$26,000 \pm 13,000$	Estimated bombardment yield	Gas counting: CO_2 in counter	[2]
$21,000 \pm 4000$	Estimated bombardment yield	a) Solid sample counting: sample with thin window counter b) Gas counting: CO_2 in counter	[3]
4700 ± 470	Mass spectrometer (1.71 per cent)	Solid carbonate counting: $BaCO_3$ with thin window counter	[4]
5300 ± 800	Mass spectrometer (3.23 and 3.35 per cent)	Solid carbonate counting: $BaCO_3$ in low absorption counter	[5]
5100 ± 200	Mass spectrometer (3.23 and 3.35 per cent)	Solid carbonate counting: $BaCO_3$ in low absorption counter	[6]
7200 ± 500	Mass spectrometer	Solid carbonate counting: $BaCO_3$ with thin window counter	[7]
6400 ± 200 or 6100 ± 200	Mass spectrometer	Gas counting (Miller technique)	[8], [9], [10], [11], [12]
5580 ± 45	Mass spectrometer	Gas counting; small amount of CO_2 in argon–alcohol gas	[13], [14]
5589 ± 75	Mass spectrometer	Gas counting; small amount of CO_2 in argon–alcohol gas	[15]
5513 ± 165	Mass spectrometer	Proportional counting of methane-CO_2 mixture	[16]
6360 ± 200	Mass spectrometer	Gas counting (Miller technique)	[8], [9], [16]
$5360 \pm (200)$†	Mass spectrometer	Gas counting (Miller technique)	[8], [9], [17]

* [1] S. Ruben and M. D. Kamen, *Phys. Rev.*, **59**, 349 (1941); [2] M. D. Kamen, *Manhattan Project Literature*, A-316; [3] A. S. Langsdorf, Jr., and R. L. Purbrick, *Manhattan Project Literature*, CP-G-3272; [4] A. F. Reid, J. R. Dunning, S. Weinhouse, and A. V. Grosse, *Phys. Rev.*, **70**, 431 (1946); [5] L. D. Norris and M. G. Inghram, *Phys. Rev.*, **70**, 772 (1946); [6] L. D. Norris and M. G. Inghram, *Phys. Rev.*, **73**, 350 (1948); [7] L. Yaffe and Jean Grunlund, *Phys. Rev.*, **74**, 696 (1948); [8] W. W. Miller, *Science*, **105**, 123 (1947); [9] S. C. Brown and W. W. Miller, *Rev. Sci. Inst.*, **18**, 496 (1947); [10] R. C. Hawkings, R. F. Hunter, W. B. Mann, and W. H. Stevens, *Phys. Rev.*, **74**, 696 (1948); [11] R. C. Hawkings, R. F. Hunter, W. B. Mann, and W. H. Stevens, *Can. J. Research*, **B,27**, 545 (1949); [12] R. C. Hawkings, R. F. Hunter, and W. B. Mann, *Can. J. Research*, **B,27**, 555 (1949); [13] A. G. Engelkemeir, W. H. Hamill, M. G. Inghram, and W. F. Libby, *Phys. Rev.*, **75**, 1825 (1949); [14] A. G. Engelkemeir and W. F. Libby, *Rev. Sci. Inst.*, **21**, 550 (1950); [15] W. M. Jones, *Phys. Rev.*, **76**, 885 (1949); [16] W. W. Miller, R. Ballentine, W. Bernstein, L. Friedman, A. O. Nier, and R. D. Evans, *Phys. Rev.*, **77**, 714 (1950); [17] G. G. Manov and L. F. Curtis, *Abstracts*, *118th Meeting, Am. Chem. Soc., Chicago, Sept., 1950*, p. 5p.

† The error quoted here is twice that listed in the reference and results from discussion at the meeting at which the paper was presented.

75;[5] and 5513 ± 165;[6] for a weighted average of 5568 ± 30, where the weighting was taken according to the inverse square root of the errors quoted.

In order to exhibit evidence as to the reliability of the half-life we choose, we shall discuss in a little detail the methods used in our laboratory[7] to obtain the value 5580 ± 45. These of course are very similar to the method used by Jones[8] at Los Alamos also. The first point is the evidence for the ability of the standard argon–alcohol-filled Geiger counter to record any ionization event occurring in the gas phase except for the small volumes near the end where the electrical field is reduced; in other words, the evidence for 100 per cent efficiency as one moves from the wire to the very wall of the counter. The proof is not completely rigorous, but the evidence strongly favors this conclusion. In the first place, it has been known since the discovery of Geiger counters that a counter can be made to record photoelectrons emitted from the wall if the wall is made of the proper materials. Photoelectrons cannot well have over 2 or 3 volts of kinetic energy and therefore have an extremely small range of their own and no ability to ionize the gas molecules. We therefore conclude that single electrons introduced right at the wall are recorded with a not negligible efficiency by a good Geiger counter. Further evidence on this point is that counters made with appropriate materials such as cesium-coated walls must be cooled to avoid an extraordinarily high background which is presumably due to the emission of thermionic electrons from the wall. These electrons of course have even lower energies than the photoelectrons, ranging around 0.03 ev, so again we see that electrons introduced at the very wall with energies below ionization energies can be recorded in these instruments. Neither of these arguments shows that the instrument records in the low-energy range in the wall region with 100 per cent efficiency. It does show, however, that the efficiency is not zero for even the lowest energies.

The argument as to efficiency rests almost entirely on two lines

5. W. M. Jones, *Phys. Rev.*, **76**, 885 (1949).

6. W. W. Miller, R. Ballentine, W. Bernstein, L. Friedman, A. O. Nier, and R. D. Evans, *Phys. Rev.*, **77**, 714 (1950).

7. A. G. Engelkemeir *et al.*, *Phys. Rev.*, **75**, 1825 (1949); A. G. Engelkemeir and W. F. Libby, *Rev. Sci. Inst.*, **21**, 550 (1950).

8. *Phys. Rev.*, **76**, 885 (1949).

of evidence. The first is an experiment in which three counters are set in a line with their axes parallel and connected electrically so that, when the first and third counters fire simultaneously, observation is made as to whether the middle counter fires.[9] The simultaneous firing of the first and third counters is due to a penetrating radiation which passes through both instruments, presumably in a straight line, and therefore certainly passes through the middle counter. These observations show that the middle counter does fire. The middle counter then is displaced in a direction perpendicular to the line joining the first and third by a small amount, and the observation repeated. The displacement is continued until the very edge of the counter just is in line with the very edges of the first and third counters. It is then found that there is a very abrupt disappearance of sensitivity of the middle counter. Further evidence has been obtained in our own researches, as described later, in which we shield the counter measuring our samples from penetrating cosmic radiation by surrounding it with a single layer of counters in tangential contact. In a typical experiment we find that without the shielding counters connected our central working counter records a rate of some 120 counts per minute, whereas the rate is reduced to about 7 counts per minute by connecting the shielding counters. The residual 7 counts per minute may well be due to contamination in our central counter or to radiation coming in the ends where our shielding-counter array affords incomplete coverage. We thus conclude that at least 95 per cent and probably more nearly 100 per cent of the radiations passing through the counter bundle are recorded by the counter bundle and thereby written off the record. More to the point, however, is that experiments in which we have added a second layer of counters have not significantly reduced this background. This seems to have the interpretation that counters in tangential contact possess nearly a 100 per cent efficiency throughout their volume.

The second general line of evidence is the internal consistency obtained in the measurements on the half-life of radiocarbon by using counters of various diameters, as discussed later. If the basic assumption of limited efficiency were not true, it seems clear that the consistency would be reduced. The assumption therefore was made in

9. K. Greisen and N. Nereson, *Phys. Rev.*, **62**, 316 (1942).

these researches that a standard brass-wall Geiger counter filled with argon and ethyl alcohol at typical pressures of 7 cm. of mercury pressure of argon, and 1.2 cm. of mercury pressure of ethyl alcohol would record any ionizing event that involved so much as a single ion pair in any part of the volume between the counter wire and the very surface of the brass wall.

With this assumption the task of measuring the half-life of radiocarbon is reduced to three parts. The first is to determine the end loss, that is, the effective volume at the ends of the counter where the field is so weak that radiations appearing in the gas are not recorded. The second task is to make correction for the case in which a radioactive carbon atom expels its beta ray in the direction of the wall but lies so close to the wall that it does not succeed in ionizing the counter gas before entering the wall, and then the ray enters the wall and remains in it without ejecting secondary ions from the wall. This is called the wall correction. The third task is of course to measure out a known number of radiocarbon atoms into the counter and to observe the disintegration rate. Correcting for the end and wall losses, one then can calculate the absolute disintegration rate and half-life.

The method used to obtain the end-loss correction is the obvious one of taking a set of counters of a given diameter but of different lengths, filling them with a given pressure of radioactive carbon dioxide, and observing the count rates. One then takes the difference between the rates observed for counters of two different lengths as the rate one would observe for a counter of length equal to the difference in length but with no end loss and from this calculates the end loss observed in the two counters. Using this technique and counters with flat ends made of lucite plastic plugs, so the construction of duplicate counters would be simple and the observed end corrections generally applicable, we have found that the end corrections are primarily dependent on the length-to-diameter ratio. For example, a counter 12 inches long and 2 inches in diameter has nearly the same percentage end loss as one 6 inches long and 1 inch in diameter. In addition, the correction is extraordinarily independent of energy for beta emitters up to 0.74 mev upper energy limit. Three substances were used for this study: A^{37}, which emits 2.8 kev Auger electrons; C^{14} with a beta spectrum with a 154 kev upper limit;

and Kr^{85} with a beta spectrum of 740 kev upper limit. The results are shown in Figure 5. The correction can be expressed empirically by the equation

$$y = K/ (L/D - K), \qquad (23)$$

where K has a value of 0.275 ± 0.1.[10]

The second correction on the count arises from the possibility that a radioactive carbon dioxide molecule that happens to disintegrate near the wall and to fire its disintegration electron in the direction of the wall will either fail to produce a free electron in the

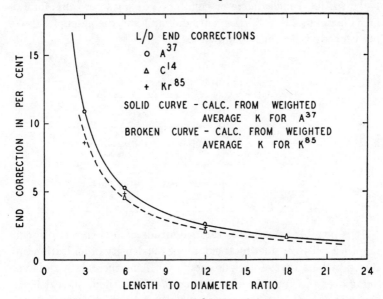

L/D END CORRECTIONS

o A^{37}

△ C^{14}

+ Kr^{85}

SOLID CURVE – CALC. FROM WEIGHTED AVERAGE K FOR A^{37}

BROKEN CURVE – CALC. FROM WEIGHTED AVERAGE K FOR K^{85}

FIG. 5.—End-loss corrections for flat-ended gas counters

gas itself or fail to dislodge one or more from the wall. At first glance this seems unlikely to be a serious effect, and it is indeed a small effect, but one large enough to require a correction. It is clear that the effect is proportional to the surface-to-volume ratio or should vary inversely as the diameter of the counter. One therefore can compare the observed count rates as a function of the diameter of the counter after the rates have been corrected for the end loss and empirically determine the magnitude of the effect. Measurements with Kr^{85} have given[11] a correction of 6.9 ± 1.1 per cent for 1-inch

10. Engelkemeir and Libby, Rev. Sci. Inst., 21, 550 (1950).   11. Ibid.

diameters, 4.6 ± 0.7 per cent for 1.5-inch diameters, and 3.4 ± 0.5 per cent for 2-inch diameter counters. It is also clear that the effect should increase with the energy of the radiation emitted, since the number of ions formed per unit length of path decreases as the energy increases. In keeping with this, no wall loss was found for the very soft 2.8-kev radiation from A^{37}. We therefore can expect that for radiocarbon with energy intermediate between these two substances the correction should be of the order of 2–4 per cent depending on the diameter of the counter. The C^{14} data themselves indicate this to be so: for 1-inch diameter counters 3.5 ± 1.2 per cent; for 1.5-inch diameters 2.3 ± 0.8 per cent; and for 2-inch diameters 1.8 ± 0.6 per cent are the values found.

TABLE 5

CALCULATED WALL CORRECTIONS

ISOTOPE	WALL LOSS CORRECTION	
	For Diameter = 1 Inch	For Diameter = 2 Inches
A^{37}	0	0
C^{14}	3.1% ±0.8	1.5% ±0.4
Kr^{85}	7.1 ±1.4	3.5 ±0.7

It is possible to estimate the magnitude of this correction semi-empirically by considering the data for the density of ionization produced by beta rays of various energies.[12] Using these data and averaging over the known beta spectrum of radiocarbon, one calculates the mean thickness of the gas near the wall which fails to count. This is a fictitious physical concept, of course, since part of the gas even next to the wall will fire its beta rays into the main body of the counter and certainly record a count. The second component of the semi-empirical calculation is the effect of splashing-out of secondary electrons by the electron incident on the wall. Data for this phenomenon are known for brass surfaces,[13] since they are of great importance in the operation of the standard photomultiplier tube. The results of this calculation are given in Table 5.

It is interesting to see how well the semi-empirically calculated corrections agree with those observed experimentally. The first half-

12. *Ibid.*   13. *Ibid.*

life published on the basis of the data obtained was 5720 ± 47 years,[14] in which the wall correction had not been made. The reality of this correction was revealed by later research,[15] and a correction of some 2.5 per cent was made to lower the value to 5580 ± 45 years.

The radioactive carbon dioxide used in the determination was obtained from the Isotopes Division of the Atomic Energy Commission, and four master-samples of carbon dioxide of different isotopic composition were prepared. These were carefully analyzed for the C^{14} contents on the mass spectrograph. The four masters were then diluted by various factors to provide seven working samples. Since the original compositions were in the range of from 1 to 6 per cent, dilution factors of several thousand fold were necessary to lower the specific radioactivity of the carbon dioxide to a measurable value. The dilution was accomplished by allowing part of the master-sample to expand from its storage bulb into a McLeod gauge. A 0.3281-cc. bulb had been sealed to the capillary of the McLeod, and the radioactive CO_2 was forced into this bulb by raising the mercury. The vacuum line was thoroughly evacuated and the pressure of CO_2 in the bulb measured. Inert CO_2 was then used to flush the vacuum line, and a pressure of inert CO_2 was allowed to build up so that, as the mercury was lowered, inert CO_2 was forced through the mercury into the McLeod to a pressure of 40 or 50 cm. of mercury. The vacuum line then was evacuated, and the total pressure in the 503.1-cc. McLeod volume was measured. After allowing to stand to mix, the diluted sample was stored in a bulb by condensation into a trap attached to the bulb using liquid nitrogen. The temperature of the room was recorded throughout the process, and it was considered that no significant error was introduced in the dilution step.

The diluted working sample was introduced into the counter in a number of different ways. The most satisfactory of the procedures was to introduce a known pressure into a rather large bulb to which a known pressure of argon was then added. After thorough mixing, this gas mixture was then introduced into the counter, to which some 1.2 cm. of ethanol vapor had previously been added. The count rate then was determined to a fraction of a per cent error, external standards being used to check that the counter was operating with its usual efficiency and corrections being made for loss due to a count

14. Engelkemeir *et al.*, *Phys. Rev.*, **75**, 1825 (1949).
15. Engelkemeir and Libby, *Rev. Sci. Inst.*, **21**, 550 (1950).

occurring while the counter was busy with the preceding count (this correction in general was quite small). Somewhat over a hundred measurements of this sort were made in the course of a two-year period, resulting in the value 5580 ± 45 mean solar years.

The agreement between our determination and those of Jones[16] and Miller et al.[17] is gratifying and leads us to believe that the weighted mean of these three determinations, 5568 ± 30, is probably accurate to within 50 years and almost certainly to within 100 years. The importance of an accurate value for the half-life to the radiocarbon dating technique is obvious, it being true that a 1 per cent error in the half-life appears immediately as a 1 per cent error in the absolute age of any given sample. For example, a 10,000-year-old sample could never be measured to better than 100 years under such conditions. It is also equally clear that a chronology could be developed in which the radiocarbon half-life was defined to be 5568, and questions of simultaneity would not be incorrect even though the half-life were indeed quite erroneous.

A further point in favor of a half-life somewhere between 5000 and 6000 years is the result obtained with ancient samples of historically known age (Fig. 1). One cannot use these data to decide definitely between the various determinations of the half-life given in the latter part of Table 4. It is conceivable that a careful research devoted entirely to the most careful measurement of the specific activity of the historically dated samples would give data of such accuracy as to distinguish between these values. Our own experience has been that the fit of the data we obtained when we thought the life to be 5720[18] was not any worse than the one obtained at present with the new life 2.5 per cent lower.[19]

It is to be hoped that further measurements on the half-life of radiocarbon will be made, preferably by entirely different techniques, since considerable agreement by the present technique we favor has already been obtained. This is important not only for the radiocarbon dating technique but for many problems in nuclear physics and radiochemistry, where methods of measuring absolute disintegration rates rather than relative rates are of vital importance.

16. *Phys. Rev.*, **76**, 885 (1949).   17. *Phys. Rev.*, **77**, 714 (1950).

18. W. F. Libby, E. C. Anderson, and J. R. Arnold, *Science*, **109**, 227 (1949).

19. J. R. Arnold and W. F. Libby, *Science*, **110**, 678 (1949).

CHAPTER IV

PREPARATION OF THE SAMPLE
FOR MEASUREMENT *

ONE of the principal requirements of the radiocarbon dating technique is that the material measured contain the original carbon atoms present in the sample at the time it died or was deposited from the exchange reservoir. This means, of course, that the chemical form in which the carbon is bonded may have real bearing on the validity of the result obtained. Chemical experience clearly indicates that the covalently bonded molecules which constitute the organic world are less susceptible of replacement of the carbon atoms by direct exchange than are the inorganic molecules such as the carbonates. One therefore does not fear particularly the possibility that the carbon in carbonate, bicarbonate, or carbon dioxide will exchange with the carbon atoms in organic structures such as wood or flesh or cloth or charcoal. One does worry considerably, however, about the possibility that underground waters washing over shell would cause an exchange.

On the other hand, putrefaction and chemical alteration are possible with organic systems, and one has to worry about whether a given sample has been so altered. Of course it is obvious that in a rich find where materials of various chemical forms exist one has an excellent opportunity to test whether alteration has occurred by observing whether the radiocarbon ages obtained from the various chemicals present in the site agree. It is clear that, if agreement is found, alteration has not occurred, for it is extremely unlikely that shell and wood would be altered to the same degree, the chemical reactions involved being so different in character.

If one examines the nature of putrefaction reactions, one observes that, by and large, they involve a degradation of molecular weights. That is, large molecular structures are reduced in size, and certain structures are so large as to not be involved. Among these latter, charcoal is most important. One does not anticipate that charcoal will be altered by any sort of attack of organic systems. About all

* See Addendum to Chapter IV, p. x above.

that can conceivably happen is that it would be burned to gaseous carbon monoxide and carbon dioxide and so escape, but it seems clear that, if one does find carbonized material and carefully removes other material from it, alteration in the residual carbon is extremely unlikely from a chemical and biochemical point of view. Materials such as wood, grass, and frozen flesh are most debatable. However, wood consists largely of very large cellulose molecules, and, if one were to take care to separate the smaller molecules from wood, it seems very likely that alteration would be definitely excluded. Likewise similar processing of fibrous materials such as grass would be a good precaution.

In the case of shell material there is no chemical guaranty that the material has not been altered. It does appear, however, from results of ours on radiocarbon content in ancient shells found together with organic matter, and results of Professor Urey on the O^{18} content of the oxygen in the carbonated shells,[1] that shells which appear well preserved physically have a good chance of being authentic. More work is needed on this point, however, and at the present time it is difficult to say of any given case whether shells will give reliable results. We look for evidences of alteration such as a powdery appearance or chalky consistency.

Our experience on woods and grasses and even peat material has been quite favorable in that we have very few evidences of alteration and some rather striking examples of organic matter such as twigs and leaves which have lain in the ground for over 10,000 years and been bathed by the underground waters, which apparently give reliable results in that they check with well-preserved pieces of wood found with them and also with the general stratigraphy and chronology built up by the whole set of dates. We are therefore inclined to recommend the materials normally found in about the following order:

1. Charcoal or charred organic material such as heavily burned bone
2. Well-preserved wood
3. Grasses, cloth, and peat
4. Well-preserved antler and similar hairy structures
5. Well-preserved shell

1. H. C. Urey, *Science*, **108**, 489 (1948); J. M. McCrea, *J. Chem. Phys.*, **18**, 849 (1950); S. Epstein *et al.*, *Bull. Geol. Soc. Am.*, **62**, 417 (1951); H. C. Urey *et al.*, *Bull. Geol. Soc. Am.*, **62**, 399 (1951).

We have had no experience with bone as such and believe that it is a very poor prospect for two reasons: the carbon content of bone is extremely low, being largely in inorganic form in a very porous structure; and it is extremely likely to have suffered alteration. It is barely conceivable that measurements on bone might reveal that some reliability could be obtained. However, because the quantities required are so large, and there usually are other acceptable materials associated with a find of bone, it does not seem to be an urgent matter to pursue.

Deevey *et al.*[2] have shown that a consideration of Godwin's[3] may be important—the assumption that the carbon entering plant material and organic material in general is in equilibrium with CO_2 of the atmosphere may not be justified in the case of plant material or animal matter living off of such plant material formed in hard waters in which the dissolved carbonate and bicarbonate is derived from ancient limestone. Direct tests on the plants grown in such an environment (Queechy Lake, N.Y.) showed that the radiocarbon content was definitely lower than normally observed in the biosphere. The conditions under which these samples were taken were rather unusual, and it is to be hoped that this additional source of error will not seriously restrict the samples which can be used for dating.

It is to be realized of course that our experiences with various types of samples must be taken in the light of the actual chemical processing we have used in the preparation of the samples for measurement. A description of this process follows.[4]

1. The first step in each instance is carefully to examine the sample and to separate out as well as possible by physical methods the material desired. For example, a piece of wood will usually be dirty and is cleaned physically as well as possible, and perhaps the surface removed by sawing or cutting so the danger of contamination is reduced. In the case of finely divided charcoal from camp fires, it is necessary carefully to remove intrusive rootlets and other matter which might introduce modern carbon into the material. It is hoped

2. E. S. Deevey, Jr., M. S. Gross, G. E. Hutchinson, and H. L. Kraybill, *Proc. Nat. Acad. Sci.*, **40**, 285 (1954).

3. H. Godwin, *Am. J. Sci.*, **249**, 301 (1951).

4. E. C. Anderson, J. R. Arnold, and W. F. Libby, *Rev. Sci. Inst.*, **22**, 225 (1951).

that eventually physical separation methods may be developed to the point where rather low carbon-containing soils can be examined.

2. The physically cleaned sample is then tested with hydrochloric acid solution for calcium carbonate which may have been deposited in the cracks and internal fissures by underground waters. If any effervescence of carbon dioxide is observed on this test, the sample then is treated for several hours with about 1 N hydrochloric acid until effervescence ceases, after which it is carefully washed and dried in a laboratory oven. This is a particularly important part of the processing and should be conducted with real care. In the case of materials containing considerable extraneous matter other than the desired organic substances, the acid treatment frequently works to purify the sample. For example, burned bone is treated with 1–3 N hydrochloric acid for 24 or 48 hours until the bone structure is dissolved, and the residual carbon, which of course does not dissolve in acid, is then removed by filtration. In one or two cases colloidal organic substances formed as a result of treatment of charred bone, and this material was separated by dialysis of the acid solution which concentrated the colloidal organic material and allowed separation and drying and use of this fraction.

This acid treatment probably guarantees to a considerable extent against the incorporation of putrefaction products in that it would heavily weigh against small organic molecules in that they would be dissolved out as gases or resist the filtration or dialysis steps.

3. This step consists of the controlled combustion of the sample, if it is organic in character, to form carbon dioxide, or the addition of hydrochloric acid to evolve carbon dioxide if the sample is shell. Figure 6 displays the apparatus in which the present step and several of the subsequent steps in the procedure are conducted. The combustion of the sample is carried out in the Vycor tube (A). Oxygen from a standard commercial cylinder is passed over the sample at a pressure slightly below 1 atmosphere, and the combustion gases are carried through hot copper oxide heated in a Vycor tube by a furnace (B) to complete the oxidation by converting carbon monoxide and possibly other gases to carbon dioxide. The gas stream then is led through a dry-ice trap and Drierite tube to remove residual water. Following this the gas is led through a controlling stopcock (D) into two successive liquid nitrogen traps (C), in which the carbon dioxide is condensed. The combustion is begun by setting the flow rate with the control stopcock (D) while air is passing through the system such that the pressure in the trap system is about 10 cm. of mercury with the high vacuum exhaust pump (1) full on. Oxygen then is admitted and the flow adjusted through a needle valve to maintain the pressure in the combustion system at slightly below 1 atmosphere. The oxidation is begun by igniting the sample with a torch applied externally. Some of the early combustions were conducted in an apparatus different from the Vycor tube (A),[5] in which the sample was placed on the top of a vertically

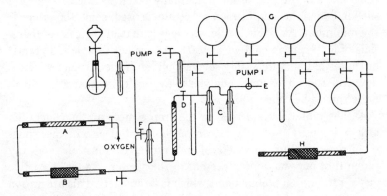

Fig. 6.—Combustion and reduction line assembly

traveling screw adjustable in position and the fire started on the top end of the sample and the screw rotated to bring fresh sample into the flame zone as combustion proceeded. The whole assembly was inclosed in a glass bulb to which the product oxygen was fed and from which the product gases were removed continuously. The oxygen was introduced with little jets near the flame zone. This apparatus is a slight modification of a standard apparatus used for ashing samples of organic matter for the detection of traces of iodine.[6] The important feature of the device is that only the portion of the

5. E. C. Anderson, Ph.D. thesis, University of Chicago (1949); *Ann. Rev. Nuc. Sci.*, **2**, 63 (1953).

6. G. M. Karns, *Ind. Eng. Chem., Anal. Ed.*, **4**, 299 (1932); H. van Kolnitz and R. E. Remington, *Ind. Eng. Chem., Anal. Ed.*, **5**, 38 (1933); F. X. Gassner, *Ind. Eng. Chem., Anal. Ed.*, **12**, 120 (1940).

sample actually burning is heated appreciably and that the hot gases do not pass over the unburned portions of the sample. It was particularly valuable in the combustion of flesh and similar materials. However, the bulk of the samples are handled in the Vycor tube (A).

The amount of material selected for combustion, or acidification in the case of shell, is determined by the carbon content of the material. It must be such as to yield between 10 and 12 grams of elementary carbon, which is equivalent to some 24 liters of carbon dioxide gas. In the case of pure charcoal, of course, 10 or 12 grams would be sufficient. Actually the charcoal is rarely this pure; something like a half-ounce or more is usually taken. In the case of pure shell in which the acidification procedure is used, some 100 grams is the minimum. As a rough rule we suggest that in the case of materials of high carbon content at least 1 ounce per sample (28 grams) be submitted and preferably several ounces. If the carbon content is doubtful and no accurate analysis is available, at least a pound or more should be collected.

4. The material condensed in the trap system at the conclusion of a run consists not only of carbon dioxide but also of the oxides of nitrogen, sulfur, products of incomplete combustion, and any radon that may have been present in the sample. Radon is a noble gas of rather high boiling point which is a radioactive disintegration product of uranium, the ubiquitous parent of most of the radioactivity in soils and rocks. This might well follow through the subsequent steps of the procedure and lead to a falsely radioactive final product if chemical purification were not used. The chemical purification therefore accomplishes the removal of the bulk of contamination consisting of oxides of nitrogen and sulfur and the trace radiochemical contamination by radon. The purification is accomplished in the following manner: A 1-liter flask containing 500 cc. of 6 N NH_4OH is attached to the stopcock at point E. After the traps have been pumped down at liquid nitrogen temperature, the Dewars are removed and the carbon dioxide is evolved, using a flame to speed up the process. When the pressure reaches 60 cm. of mercury, the trap system is connected to the flask. A rapid absorption of the gas takes place. The evolution of the gas is continued, and the flask is shaken to insure absorption until the traps are empty. The pressure at this point should be about 70 cm. of mercury, and the solution should be quite hot. A second solution consisting of 180 grams of $CaCl_2 \cdot 2H_2O$ in 180 cc. of water is heated near to boiling. The flask is removed from the line, and the hot calcium chloride solution is added slowly from a separatory funnel. Rapid precipitation of calcium carbonate takes place. It is essential that this step be carried out in such a way that the final temperature of the combined solution be higher than 70° C. Otherwise a flocculent, poorly filterable precipitate results. The precipitate is filtered and washed free of ammonia, the washings being made with distilled water. It is then removed from the Buchner funnel used for the filtration and washed into a clean 1-liter flask. At this point all the oxides have been left behind in the form of soluble salts, and the radon has been lost either by gaseous evolution or in the aqueous solution.

Carbon dioxide now is removed from the precipitate, using the same system employed in the combustion. A separatory funnel containing 250 cc. of concentrated hydrochloric acid is placed in the flask. A second lead is attached to the drying and collection system at F. It is important that the tube from the separatory funnel reach nearly to the bottom of the flask to prevent the accumulation of acid and uneven reaction. In the beginning of this operation the gas-flow rate is set as in the combustion operation. The stopcock leading to the flask is opened, and acid is added at a rate sufficient to keep the pressure in the flask slightly below 1 atmosphere.

The gas is dried carefully and collected in the traps (C) and then allowed to evaporate into a system of 5-liter bulbs (G), where it is stored ready for the reduction step.

5. Reduction is carried out in an iron tube (H), which is filled with about 85 grams of magnesium turnings together with 1 gram of cadmium powder or turnings as a catalyst. An 8-inch movable electric furnace capable of reaching 1000° C. is placed around the tube. The ends of the tube are sealed with rubber stoppers and deKhotinsky wax, and the reduction system evacuated and tested for freedom from leaks.

Carbon dioxide is now admitted to the tube up to a pressure approaching 1 atmosphere and external heat applied with a torch at one end of the magnesium filling. When a temperature near the melting point of magnesium (660° C.) is reached, the reaction begins rather violently and produces sufficient heat to maintain itself if gas is admitted at a moderate rate from the bulbs. The chemical reaction involved is

$$2 \text{ Mg} + \text{CO}_2 = 2 \text{ MgO} + \text{C} . \tag{24}$$

Since the reaction involves no gaseous products, no circulation is required, and care must be taken because the heat evolved is so large that, unless the inflow of carbon dioxide is controlled, the reaction will melt the iron tube. It is a practice to run in gas from one bulb in a controlled fashion. The carbon dioxide in the storage bulbs is introduced into the reduction chamber one bulb at a time until pressure is reduced to about 20 cm. of mercury in each. In this way five or six bulbs of gas can be reacted smoothly before the other end of the magnesium filling is reached. To complete the reduction, the remaining gas is condensed in the trap (J) and may either be expanded into a single bulb or reacted directly. It is necessary to apply external heat using the furnace to start the fire again after this collection of the residual carbon dioxide in the various bulbs. When the reaction is complete, no more than 1 or 2 cm. of mercury pressure should remain in the manifold system, and the bulbs should be completely empty. The reduction tube then is allowed to cool, and the carbon, magnesium oxide, and unreacted magnesium are removed from the tube, using an iron rod as a ram.

6. The material taken from the reduction tube is placed in a clean 3-liter beaker. Sufficient distilled water is added to dampen, and the mixture is allowed to stand 15 minutes until the hydrocarbons which are formed in small yield, presumably by the impurities in the magnesium metal, are decomposed and evolved. Concentrated hydrochloric acid then is added as rapidly as possible without bubbling over. The proper rate for this is about 25 cc. every 5 minutes. After about 100 cc. have been added in the first 20 minutes, an additional 700 cc. is added rapidly. It is well to have a spare 3-liter beaker handy in case of overflow at this point.

The acid solution is allowed to stand overnight in a hood so the fumes evolved are exhausted from the room. It is then placed on a hot plate with an asbestos pad over the plate at "high" heat. After the acid is brought to a boil, about 1 liter of distilled water is added, and the solution brought to a boil and allowed to boil for about 15 minutes. It then is filtered by the insertion of a sintered glass "filter stick" made by taking a coarse sintered glass suction funnel and cutting off the rim normally used to hold the solution in the funnel down to the level of the sintered glass plate, sealing a piece of glass tubing about 6 inches long on the end of the funnel, and connecting the rubber hose to a good aspirator. This device has the advantage of removing the obnoxious acid solution without mechanical lifting and dispersing it in the sewer system immediately after dilution. It also has the merit that no new glass apparatus has to be brought into the process with its consequent danger of introducing contamination.

After sucking the black carbon residue dry, 1.5–2 liters of distilled water are added and the system again brought to a boil and allowed to boil about 15 minutes. The filtration step is then repeated, and distilled water added again and brought to a boil for the same length of time. This washing step is then repeated a third time, at which point the wet carbon is transferred to a clean 400-cc. beaker quantitatively by washing out with distilled water and finally drying roughly by the use of the filter stick. It then is placed on the hot plate on "low" heat and left there for about 4 hours, until moisture just ceases to condense on a cold watch glass.

After the drying operation the dry carbon is replaced in the original beaker, and about half a liter of concentrated hydrochloric acid is added, and the mixture allowed to stand about 2 hours. It then is brought to a boil, and the process of filtering and washing described above is repeated. After this the drying operation described above is performed again.

The sample then is placed in a clean, weighed, dry bottle with a screw cap, carefully labeled, and weighed.

7. The final step in the preparation of the sample for measurement consists of grinding in an agate mortar and pestle to a consistency approaching that of powdered sugar, returning the sample to the bottle and mixing it by shaking, after which about 0.5 gram are removed, carefully weighed, and the percentage ash in the sample determined by combustion. Care is taken during this operation to expose the sample to the air for the minimum length of time, to keep cigarette ashes and other room dust out of it, and not to breathe into it excessively. The percentage ash is necessary as a correction on the count rate observed, for, of course, the ash reduces the observed specific radioactivity.

A number of precautions are taken throughout this process. Probably the most important of these is to purchase all the chemicals in large quantities so that a single successful run with coal in which no radiocarbon is obtained will validate the purity of considerable quantities of chemicals. One can then feel free to seek sources other than the chemicals for any contamination that may appear in the sample. We have been singularly fortunate in that to date we have observed no chemical contamination of any sort. We are careful to use the same glassware that has been used in previous runs with coal samples and to be extremely cautious that the carbon is exposed to the air a minimum time while cool and dry. In fact, care is taken to bottle the carbon or to cover it with acid solution quickly after the drying period. The carbon produced in this reaction possesses an extremely high specific surface area so that its power to absorb vapors is large. Rough measurements have indicated that it possesses something over 200 square meters of surface per gram on the average. This means that any considerable exposure to room air is likely to lead to radon absorption and contamination. Of course it is almost unnecessary to say that the laboratory in which the chemical processing and the sample mounting to be described later are performed should not contain any radioactivity that is not tightly sealed and protected from access to the air. It is good practice to keep the laboratory clean of all radioactivities.

There is a considerable mystery remaining about the origin of the ash in the sample. We ordinarily find it to be less than 10 per cent, but occasionally for some unknown reason it will approach 20 per cent. We do find that unless the material is dried as described above and then re-extracted with acid, the ash usually is above 20 per cent. It is further found that a recalcitrant sample with a high ash can be successfully reduced in ash content by heating to a dull red heat in a quartz or heavy Pyrex test tube which is closed from the air with a loose glass-wool plug. The heat is continued for several hours, and acid extraction as described above is used afterward. This almost invariably reduces the ash below 10 per cent. A source of worry of some importance exists in the chemical composition of the impurities which constitute the ash. The corrections as ordinarily made assume that it is magnesium oxide—in other words, that it has the same chemical composition while in the sample as it does after ignition. Experience has shown that this method gives results which are acceptable in that the same value for the specific activity of a given original sample is obtained from two or more portions which have been burned, reduced, extracted, and measured and in which the final carbon samples obtained from the several portions have different ash contents. We would therefore suggest that the impurity is indeed in the form of magnesium oxide which is tightly covered with carbon and that the drying and heating operations described, which are observed to reduce the ash, essentially crack loose the carbon covering from the small magnesium oxide particles. It has been shown that the ash does indeed consist of magnesium oxide rather than of other materials.

A special equipment and chemicals list for the operations described above is given in Appendix A.

The recently developed gas counting methods require appropriate changes in the technique of sample preparation. Suess[7] describes preparation of the acetylene samples he uses. The initial steps in the process are identical with those described above through the absorption of the carbon dioxide in the ammonium hydroxide solution except that smaller amounts of samples can be used. The proportion is about one-third. In the next step, instead of calcium chloride, strontium chloride is used to precipitate the carbonate. The strontium carbonate so obtained, after washing and drying, is directly reduced with an excess of magnesium powder (80 mesh) to strontium carbide. If enough of the material is available, a mixture of 30 grams of strontium carbonate and 35 grams of magnesium is used, yielding about 2.2 liters STP of acetylene, which corresponds to a yield of 90–100 per cent. The reaction is carried out inside an evacuated stainless-steel tube (2.8 × 38 cm.) connected directly to a vacuum line through an O-ring seal. The mixture is ignited from the outside with a torch, and the reaction is completed in less than 5 minutes. The reaction product then is dumped into about 1 liter of water inside an evacuated system. The gases formed are dried by passing them through a trap cooled by an acetone mixture and drierite. The acetylene is condensed in a liquid nitrogen trap, and some hydrogen that also forms is pumped off intermittently. After purification by passing over cooled charcoal, the acetylene is

7. H. E. Suess, *Science*, **120**, 5 (1954).

stored for 2–3 weeks to permit the decay of the few hundred radon atoms that are sometimes present in the gas sample.

For the carbon dioxide gas counting method, which depends on the proportional counting technique,[8] it is necessary to prepare extremely pure carbon dioxide because of the effects of electronegative gases on the proportional counting characteristics of the high-pressure carbon dioxide gas used in this method. The sample preparation technique is the same as that described above through the precipitation and washing of the calcium carbonate. The procedure used is that of DeVries and Barendsen.[9] Approximately 50 grams of the pure calcium carbonate is placed in a reaction vessel, which then is evacuated and the carbon dioxide liberated by the addition of aqueous citric acid. The gross part of the water vapor is removed from the gas by passage through a dry-ice–acetone trap, and the partially dried gas is conducted into a flask containing calcium oxide maintained at a temperature of 600° C. After the carbon dioxide has been absorbed in the hot calcium oxide, the dry-ice trap and reaction flask are closed off from the system. The calcium carbonate–calcium oxide mixture is then subjected to alternate periods of evacuation and standing at 600° C. During this time, water and oxygen are effectively removed from the system with little loss of sample. Pure carbon dioxide then is evolved from the calcium carbonate by raising the temperature to about 800° C. The gas is collected under continuous evacuation in a liquid nitrogen trap, from which it is allowed to vaporize into the counter to be used.

Carbon dioxide used for the Geiger counter method of measurement[10] is prepared by a procedure simpler than that described in the paragraph just preceding, in that the calcium carbonate, prepared as described earlier in this chapter, is decomposed with hydrochloric acid, and the carbon dioxide evolved is passed through two cold traps and then frozen out with liquid nitrogen. It then is evaporated directly into the counter for measurement.

8. Hl. deVries and G. W. Barendsen, *Physica*, **18**, 652 (1952); *ibid.*, **19**, 987 (1953); H. R. Brannon, M. S. Taggart, and M. Williams, private communication; G. J. Fergusson, private communication.

9. *Physica*, **18**, 652 (1952); *ibid.*, **19**, 987 (1953).

10. H. R. Crane, Andover Conference on Radiocarbon Dating, Phillips Academy, October 21–23, 1954.

CHAPTER V

MEASUREMENT OF THE SAMPLE

THE problem of detection and measurement of weakly radioactive substances is an ancient one around which a considerable lore and artistry have been built. In the case of radiocarbon at the levels existing in nature one needs to use the most sensitive techniques known. On the other hand, it is essential that the procedure be as simple and as reliable as possible. There are two obvious ways in which to proceed with the problem. One is to measure the material in the gaseous state as either carbon dioxide or methane, in which the sample being measured constitutes part of the gas phase of the detection instrument. It would seem wisest to use a proportional type counter operating at as high a pressure of methane or carbon dioxide as feasible in which the pulses due to the radiocarbon beta radiation were segregated to a certain extent from pulses of different size due to extraneous effects such as cosmic radiation and wall contamination in the apparatus. This type of attack was not pursued in this research, for calculations indicated that the second obvious approach would be somewhat more sensitive and reliable, though it would require somewhat larger samples. This consists of measuring elementary carbon itself in the solid state.

The construction of the instrument must be such as to insure the maximum ratio of count rate due to the sample to count rate due to background, that is, the cosmic radiation and apparatus and laboratory contamination. In the first place, one immediately chooses a Geiger counter as the detection instrument, since it is the only instrument which will detect a single thermal energy electron with apparently 100 per cent efficiency. This establishes it as the most sensitive of all instruments for detection of ionization. Having selected a Geiger counter, which consists in essence of a cylinder with a wire down the axis, one seeks to mount the carbon sample in the position which will insure the maximum sample effect to background ratio. It is clear from the geometry of the Geiger counter that there is only one place to do this, and that is on the wall. It is further clear that one must not interpose between the counter gas and the sample any more solid material than is necessary. Therefore, one builds the Geiger counter essentially with the elementary carbon as the wall of the counter. It is fortunate that elementary carbon is an electrical conductor.

The next problem one faces in instrument design in this problem is that of measuring the background without changing the counter gas and other critical characteristics of the instrument. In other words, one wants to change the wall of the Geiger counter from one material to another without changing the Geiger counter in essence. All these things are accomplished by the instrument known as the screen-wall counter,[1] an artist's sketch of which is shown in Figure 7.

The essential principle on which this instrument operates is that the most important part of the counting act takes place near the counter wire, and therefore the only essential requirement is that the field near the wire be undisturbed by changing the counter wall from the carbon sample to bare metal for the background measurement. This is accomplished by interposing gridwork about halfway between the counter wire and the sample cylinder which constitutes the counter wall. One then controls the potential on the screen wall. It then operates essentially as the wall of an ordinary Geiger counter with respect to the wire except that it is extremely porous to radiation. Radiations which miss the screen gridwork structure itself can be recorded, providing they enter the gas at all by the interposition of a small "drag-in" potential which serves to accelerate electrons toward the screen counter structure if they are formed in the space between the screen and sample cylinder. Conversely, if one wants to restrict the counter volume just to the screen structure, this can be done by using a "drag-out" potential. These potentials are small, of the order of 50–100 volts. Figure 8 shows the behavior of the count rate for a typical screen-wall counter of the dimensions and construction used in this research, as a function of the potential between the sample cylinder and the screen. We normally operate with 90 volts drag in potential in the radiocarbon dating work. It is obvious from Figure 8 that there is nothing critical about this number.

1. W. F. Libby, *Phys. Rev.*, **46**, 196 (1934); W. F. Libby and D. D. Lee, *Phys. Rev.*, **55**, 245 (1939).

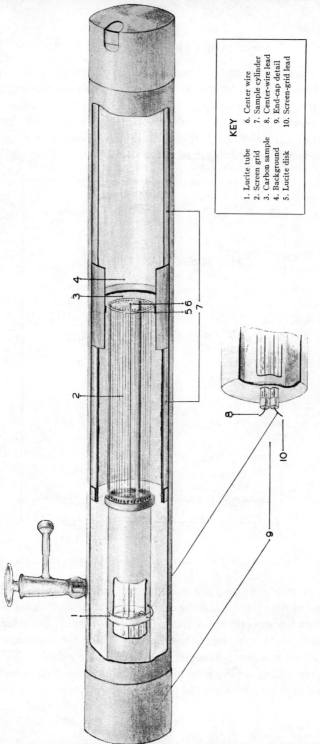

KEY

1. Lucite tube
2. Screen grid
3. Carbon sample
4. Background
5. Lucite disk
6. Center wire
7. Sample cylinder
8. Center-wire lead
9. End-cap detail
10. Screen-grid lead

FIG. 7.—Screen-wall counter

In the instrument as described, one has a cylindrical vacuum-type space filled with counter gas, along the middle third of the length of which Geiger counter registration of ionizing events take place, and inside of which a sample cylinder two-thirds as long as the instrument itself is placed. One half of the sample cylinder has the sample mounted on it; in this case elementary carbon. With these dimensions

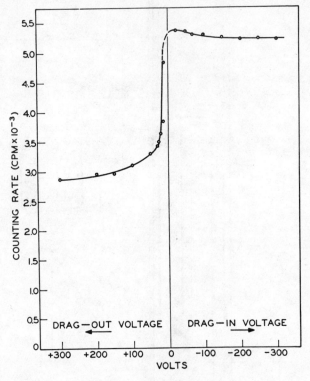

FIG. 8.—Variation of counter sensitivity with potential between screen and case

there are two positions, one in which the sample itself constitutes the wall of the counter, and the other in which the bare metal of the sample cylinder constitutes the wall of the counter. One changes from one position to the other simply by lifting the instrument in one's hands and gently shaking until the sample cylinder slides to the other end. It is purposely machined to have freedom of motion without having excessive radial play. The procedure of measurement then consists simply in observing the rate in the two positions with appropriate frequency of alteration and recording the data.

The sensitivity of the instrument to radiocarbon radiation is best established by the use of a sample assayed in an absolute manner such as that described in chapter iii. A sample of radioactive carbon dioxide of accurately known specific activity used in the half-life determination[2] was taken, accurately diluted with ordinary carbon dioxide, and then reduced and converted to a standard carbon sample in the way described in the preceding chapter. This material then was mounted and the observed count rate taken under various conditions in order to determine the absolute efficiency of the instrument for radiocarbon radiation when observed from elementary carbon samples. Several such standard radiocarbon samples were devised, and tests were carried out in four different screen-wall counters. One of the tests was made by using a sample only 1 inch in length. The standard sample cylinder is 8 inches in length, so the 1-inch sample was placed in the eight different positions, numbering from the end farthest removed from the counter volume when the sample cylinder is in the "background" position. The reasons for undertaking this test were primarily to reveal the fraction of the radiation which entered the counting volume from the background position and the variation of sensitivity at the very end of the sample cylinder. The data are given in Table 6.

These data show that the efficiency rises rather rapidly as one moves in from the end of the sample, so that only the first 1 inch is appreciably lower in efficiency than the 6 inches of sample in the central portion. It is also clear from these data that some 3-4 per cent of the net sample count that would be observed, were not the background changed by virtue of the radioactivity of the sample, acts to increase the background. Therefore, in deducing the figure by which we are to multiply the observed difference between sample and background positions to obtain the absolute specific activity of the sample, we must take the efficiency calculated from the actual difference between background and sample averaged over the various positions. This is calculated to be 5.35 ± 0.10 per cent for these data. One gram of carbon mounted on the 1-inch-long section of the

2. A. G. Engelkemeir, W. H. Hamill, M. G. Inghram, and W. F. Libby, *Phys. Rev.*, **57**, 1825 (1949).

sample cylinder had an absolute disintegration rate of 1860 disintegrations per minute.

Table 7 presents data in which a standard sample of the full 8 grams weight and mounted over the full 8 inches of length of the cylinder was placed in four different counters. The absolute efficiency calculated on the basis of the observed difference between sample

TABLE 6

EFFICIENCY OF SCREEN-WALL COUNTER ALONG ITS LENGTH
(Counter No. 6; standard 10 cm. A + 0.5 cm. C_2H_4)

Position	Background (cpm)	Sample (cpm)	Net Sample from Average Background Positions 1–5	Per Cent Absolute Efficiency	Increase in Background (Per Cent Net Sample Count)
1.........	147.4 ± 1.3	241.7 ± 1.6	95.0 ± 1.8	5.11	....
2.........	146.4 ± 1.6	257.1 ± 1.6	110.4 ± 1.8	5.94	....
3.........	145.8 ± 1.7	253.5 ± 1.5	106.8 ± 1.8	5.74	....
4.........	149.2 ± 1.9	255.9 ± 1.5	109.2 ± 1.8	5.88	....
5.........	144.9 ± 1.5	252.5 ± 1.5	105.8 ± 1.8	5.69	....
6.........	....	....	....	....	....
7.........	152.4 ± 1.5	257.8 ± 1.6	111.1 ± 1.8	5.98	5.2
8.........	169.4 ± 1.8	228.4 ± 1.4	81.7 ± 1.8	4.39	20.9
Average*...	....	....	....	5.35 ± 0.10	3.5

* Taken with actual backgrounds and not the average of positions 1–5.

TABLE 7

EFFICIENCY OF SCREEN-WALL COUNTERS

Counter	Absolute Efficiency (Per Cent of Absolute Rate)
4	5.56 ± 0.05
5	5.59 ± 0.07
6	5.36 ± 0.07
T	5.37 ± 0.07
Ring (Table 6).........	5.35 ± 0.10
Average (weighted)......	5.46 ± 0.03

and background is given. This number is used to convert the observed count rates to absolute disintegration rates.

The radiocarbon radiation has a range of some 28 mg/cm²; that is, a foil weighing 28 mg/cm² will just stop the radiation. The absorption is nearly exponential; the half-thickness, or thickness necessary to absorb half of the radiation, is about 2.3 mg/cm². It is clear, therefore, that for our sample cylinder of 400 cm.² surface area (the diameter some 2.7 inches) a layer 2.3 mg/cm² thick or a total sample of 0.92 gram of carbon would give half of the effect that an infinitely thick layer would give. The formula for this is[3]

$$\frac{I}{I_\infty} = 1 - e^{-8.7x}, \tag{25}$$

where I_∞ is the count rate that would have been obtained from a sample of infinite thickness (of thickness at least equal to the range), I is the intensity observed for the sample of given thickness, and x is the ratio of the actual thickness used to the range of the radiation. The validity of this formula has been experimentally established on a number of occasions by carefully mounting radiocarbon samples of known thicknesses less than the range and plotting the count rate observed as a function of thickness. It is apparent, however, that the formula will be valid only if the sample has uniform thickness over its entire area. Since this is a difficult condition to obtain, we have chosen to make x so large that the count rate is essentially equal to the rate for the infinitely thick layer and so to avoid worries about roughness of the sample. One can show that, if the sample appears reasonably smooth to the eye, errors due to the existence of rough spots will be very small. In general, the thickness selected has been 20 mg/cm², or a total sample weight of 8 grams for the 400 cm.² area of the sample cylinder. From time to time samples have been used which did not amount to 8 grams, the smallest being about 5 grams. These were mounted with considerable care to insure uniformity, and then the count rate was corrected by the small factor given by Equation (25). It seems possible that one might measure samples much smaller than 5 grams by developing a technique of painting the carbon on the brass cylinder in a very reproducible and smooth fashion.

The carbon sample is mounted on one half of the sample cylinder (the sample cylinder is split so that the counting operation can be conducted with convenience and the cylinder reassembled later). The other half of the sample cylinder remains bare. Figure 9 shows the equipment used, together with the two halves of the brass sample cylinder. As described earlier, the carbon sample in the screw-capped

3. W. F. Libby, *Anal. Chem.*, **19**, 2 (1947).

Fig. 9.— Sample mounting display

glass bottle is ground carefully in a mortar and pestle, about 8.5 grams weighed out in a beaker, and some 50–55 cc. of distilled water added. The mixture then is stirred and water added until a consistency like a very thin mush is obtained. One then places a clean white glove on his left hand (if he is right-handed) and, holding the beaker and the sample cylinder in his left hand in such a way that the contents can run from the beaker into the sample cylinder, elevates it toward a light such as an open window so that he can observe the sample flow from the beaker into the cylinder and also scrape out the remnants with a long glass rod. He then replaces the beaker on the table and with the glass rod smooths the sample while rotating the cylinder with his left hand. He then takes the spatula and scrapes out the residual carbon left in the beaker (usually something around 0.5 gram of carbon is left either in the beaker or on the rod) and smooths this onto the surface also. In the early work we used about 20 cc. of 0.15 per cent agar solution to increase the adherence of the sample to the wall. It was found, however, that this was unnecessary providing one was careful not to bump or bang the instrument, and this potential source of contamination was thereby avoided. After the wet carbon sample is smoothed on the cylinder, it is placed on a clean piece of cheesecloth on the table and an ordinary hair-dryer used to blow hot air through it for about 10 minutes. This removes sufficient water to set the sample on the cylinder and yet does not dry the sample completely. It is important that the sample not be dried too long with the hot-air stream for two reasons. The first is that air contains radon, and the sample, if dried, will be extremely susceptible to contamination by absorption of the radon and other possible radioactivities in the air. The carbon samples have large surface areas per gram (of the order of 200 square meters). The second reason is that the warm air has an oxidative action on the brass when the metal gets warm and causes leaching of the zinc out of the brass into the absorbent-carbon sample, so that the ash rises to unreasonable values.

After the drying to the setting stage, the two halves of the sample cylinder are placed together, sometimes fastened with a small piece of Scotch tape if they do not fit snugly, and the sample cylinder placed in the counter proper. The counter cap is then placed on and the counter sealed closed with deKhotinsky wax. The counter then is placed on a standard vacuum line with two liquid nitrogen traps in series, the first of which has had the internal tube removed so blocking by the ice condensed does not occur readily, and the system allowed to pump for about 24 hours, the nitrogen in the traps being renewed from time to time. At the end of this pumping period the pressure in the line as registered by a Pirani gauge placed between the counter and the first trap will read in the micron range. It is important to remove water to this degree, for, if it is not done, the water absorbed on the sample will slowly evolve and change the operating voltage of the counter during the measurement period. After pumping, 0.5 cm. of ethylene is added. The ethylene is purified by repeated condensation in a liquid nitrogen trap, pumping on the solid, re-evaporation, recondensation, etc., until the vacuum obtained while pumping on the frozen ethylene rapidly approaches a few microns. After the ethylene is introduced, 10 cm. of argon from a standard commercial cylinder of pure argon is added. The counter then is allowed to stand for 2 or 3 hours for mixing, and the voltage measured at which pulses of 6 volts height are obtained. One can run the plateau at this stage, but it is soon found that the plateau characteristics are very reproducible, and this step usually is not taken. The appearance of the pulses on an oscilloscope is observed with care. The oscilloscope is connected so the true pulse shape is shown rather than the first time derivative. This is accomplished by connecting the wall of the counter to ground through a resistor, the potential drop across which is fed to the oscilloscope. Choice of the proper resistor insures that the time constant of the oscilloscope circuit is short enough to afford faithful pulse reproduction. It is particularly important to examine the pulses for multiplicity. The occurrence of multiple pulses is undesirable not only because it is evidence of improper gas composition but primarily because the cancellation of meson counts by the anticoincidence shielding counters will not occur for multiple pulses. The first component of the multiple pulses is canceled, but the following pulses occur later and are not canceled. This means, of course, that the background rate is observed to rise when impurities such as air or water vapor are introduced into the counter gas. The instrument at this stage is ready for placing in the shield and the beginning of the measurement run.

The counter construction is shown in Figure 7. Standard blueprints can be obtained from the author on request. The materials used in the construction of the counter, and also the shield described later, are given in Appendix B, together with the suppliers we have used. The gridwork is constructed by stringing wires between lucite header disks and the whole assembly is supported on a post, silver-soldered to one of the two end caps. Lead-free brass tubing is used both for the material of the cylinder case and the other brass parts and for the sample cylinder. This precaution is taken to avoid radioactive contamination. The cylinder wall is made as thin as convenient in order to improve the efficiency of the anticoincidence shielding described later. A glass stopcock is fastened by deKhotinsky wax to the outlet shown, and this wax is used for all the other closures also. We have constructed one or two instruments with rubber gasket seals at the ends, but in most of the counters we have used wax seals.

The deKhotinsky wax used is made by cooking together approximately equal parts of Georgia pine tar and orange shellac. The mixture is melted, heated, and stirred continuously for about 30 minutes, care being taken not to char. This wax is particularly strong and has proved eminently satisfactory. It is applied with an air-gas torch. One should not use an oxygen torch because charring of the wax will be likely. It is difficult to obtain vacuum-tight seals when the wax is charred. The parts to be sealed are heated above the softening point of the wax and the wax applied by touching to the hot metal or glass. One can also heat the wax stick briefly (the wax is poured from the cooking pot onto metal foils which are then rolled to make sticks about 6 inches long and $\frac{1}{2}$ inch in diameter) directly and let it drip onto the hot metal. The counter is then rotated so that a smooth and uniform layer of wax is obtained, and the seal is cooled by blowing air on it. Our experience has been that vacuum-tight seals can be obtained easily in this manner, and the only difficulty encountered in the use of the instrument so far as vacuum is concerned is that one occasionally breaks the wax seal by bumping the sample cylinder too vigorously against the end caps. This, however, is undesirable from the point of view of dislodging the sample itself and should be avoided.

The principal task in the measurement of extremely small

amounts of radioactivity remaining after one has supplied a sufficiently sensitive counter is the reduction of the extraneous background count rate due to cosmic radiation and the ubiquitous radioactive products of uranium and thorium which exist in all laboratories in such amounts as to give very appreciable count rates. The latter component of the background is best removed by selecting solid material which is free of uranium and thorium and of its disintegration products such as radon. Consideration of this problem, together with the problem of cost, has led us to believe that steel should be an excellent material for a low-level counter shield. It is reasonably inexpensive and from the metallurgical processing involved in its manufacture should be relatively free of the highly electropositive elements which constitute the most serious radioactive contaminates. It is reasoned that elements such as uranium, thorium, and radium will be removed by the slagging operation. We do not believe that lead is particularly desirable from either the cost or the cleanliness point of view, and tests have confirmed the suspicion of radioactive contamination in lead as ordinarily purchased. We have constructed the shield as shown in Figure 10, of hot rolled steel plate, 8 inches thick. Two types have been built, in one of which the door is closed by the hydraulic jack shown, and another in which the door is bisected and opened with a cantilever arrangement by hand.

The background rate for the unshielded screen-wall counter is in the vicinity of 500 counts per minute. Placing the instrument in the shield with 8 inches of iron in all directions reduces this to 100 counts per minute. If instead of the 8-inch shield one uses a shield with 4-inch walls outside of which 2 inches of lead are placed, the background is 120 counts per minute. This residual background is very large due to the cosmic-ray mesons whose penetrating power is very great. It would be removed only by very great thicknesses of shield material. The device used to eliminate this component of the background consists of surrounding the screen-wall counter with a complete layer of Geiger counters 18 inches in length, 2 inches in diameter, which are in tangential contact and are placed as shown in Figure 11. This is an end-on view of the assembly in place with the door of the shield open. When the shielding counters fire, the central screen-wall counter is inactivated for a small fraction of a second. This means that the meson radiation is thereby eliminated from the record. The aggregate count rate of the eleven shield counters is about 800 per minute, and the cancellation time is of the order of 10^{-3} seconds so the screen-wall counter is inactivated for about 1 per cent of the time. This is so small as to be negligible, and we can conclude therefore that the sensitivity of the

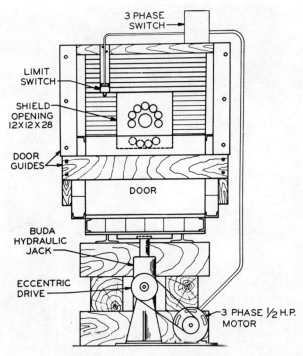

FIG. 10.—Schematic of counters and shield

apparatus to the radiocarbon radiation from the sample is not appreciably reduced by the use of the shielding counter area. The use of the shielding counters reduces the background to 5 counts per minute. The smaller shield mentioned above with 4-inch thick iron and 2-inch lead exterior gives 7 counts per minute. With these rates it is now possible to measure the radiocarbon radiation to about 2 per cent error in 48 hours. Modern wood gives 6.7 counts above the background, so that one observes a rate of 11.7 with the carbon sample in place and a rate of 5 counts per minute with the bare cylinder in place. The anticoincidence shielding counters are 18 inches long, thereby considerably overhanging the sensitive volume of the screen wall, which is 8 inches in length. We therefore have not placed a layer of shielding counters at either end of the assembly. It is clear, of course, that this would reduce the background further, but the

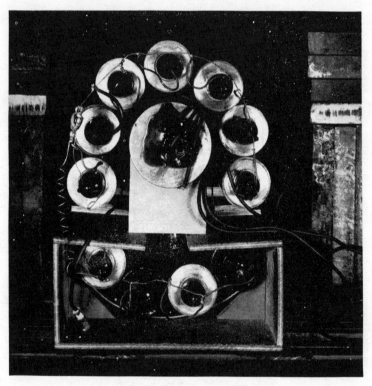

Fig. 11.—Counters in shield (door open)

extra mechanical difficulties involved in changing the sample cylinder and the small advantages to be gained by further lowering of the background have prevented our doing so. The shielding counters used are standard brass-wall cosmic-ray counters sold by commercial suppliers.

The operation of the screen-wall counter in the manner described for the measurement of radiocarbon in the age-measurement program involves several sorts of difficulties, one of which is major and which deserves special mention. Counters which have accidentally been connected incorrectly so that the leads from the screen wall and the counter wire are interchanged, and have been maintained in this condition for some time, have a tendency to show spurious counts for some time thereafter. It seems that the only way in which this can be cured, other than by allowing the instrument to stand for weeks, is to replace the lucite insulators. This point, however, is not completely settled; it is merely known that this accomplishes the results. A similar effect may be produced by erroneous application of excessive potentials so that the counter goes into essentially continuous discharge. One should take care to have a connector plug connecting the counter leads to the amplifier and recording apparatus such that this error is not possible.

Any good quenching vapor is satisfactory for the screen-wall counter as far as counting characteristics are concerned, but a consideration of some subtlety is involved which leads one to select ethylene. In our case, where the sample of carbon is very finely divided and possesses a very high absorptive power for condensible vapors such as ethanol, the amount of quenching gas absorbed may be such as appreciably to affect the fraction of the radiation which escapes the sample and reaches the counter gas volume. In the case of ethyl alcohol our experience has been that as much as 1 gram was absorbed on our standard 8-gram sample. This, of course, in addition to absorbing the radiation, may introduce radiation itself, depending on whether the ethanol is grain alcohol or synthetic. The early measurements were made with ethyl alcohol, and the corrections for the specific activity of the ethyl alcohol and its absorptive action on the radiations from the carbon sample computed. The results were acceptable, but an additional error was introduced. For these reasons a quenching gas of lower boiling point was sought, and ethylene[4] has proved to be completely satisfactory in all respects. As mentioned above, the standard filling is 0.5 cm. of mercury pressure of ethylene and 10 cm. of mercury pressure of argon.

We have not found it necessary to purify the commercial argon but have taken the precaution of buying large 200-cubic-foot cylinders so that satisfactory operation is guaranteed for an extended

4. K. H. Morgenstern, C. L. Cowan, and E. L. Hughes, *Phys. Rev.*, **74**, 499 (1948).

period if a good cylinder is obtained. It has been our experience that the argon available on the commercial market is sufficiently pure.

Interesting effects arise if the counter happens to develop a leak. The introduction of air to the counter gas adds to the normal single sharp pulses a group of smaller pulses following the original one after a delay of several hundred microseconds. This may be sufficiently long to extend beyond the cancellation period given by the anti-coincidence shielding counters, so that a pulse which would normally have been canceled from the record registers. One therefore observes a rise in background count together with a rise in the counter voltage and, at appreciable air contaminations, a decrease in the difference between the sample and background counts. This decrease is apparently due to inefficiency in the counter action caused by the presence of the air; presumably the oxygen in the air is the active agent. The decrease probably arises in the volume between the screen and wall, where the collecting field is lowest.

A further effect of some importance to routine operation exists in the temperature dependence of the operating voltage of the counter. It is found that a temperature variation of 10° F. will cause 10 or 20 volts change in the counter voltage. This may be due to the temperature dependence of the absorption of ethylene on the highly absorptive carbon sample. It means that one should take care to insure that the room temperature does not vary by more than 5° F. during long operating periods when the rate is not being recorded.

It has been our practice to change the sample cylinder from one position to the other every few hours during the day and to allow it to run during an 8- or 10-hour period overnight, arranging the schedule so that the total time spent counting the sample and the background will be proportional to the square roots of the rates in the two positions. This, for example, means that for a measurement of modern wood, where the background rate is about half the rate in the sample position, 60 per cent of the time is spent measuring the sample and 40 per cent measuring the background. In addition, of course, the background count from run to run should check nearly within the statistical error of the counts. One is tempted to cross-average the background counts and thereby to reduce the time necessary to measure. We have never done so, however, for it has been observed that changes in the operating characteristics of the shielding counters may occur which will affect both the background and the sample rate in the same way and not invalidate the difference, though it might cause as much as a half-count per minute change in both rates.

The final cleaning of the sample cylinder before use in the first instance consists in washing in 50 per cent nitric acid, rinsing carefully with distilled water, and drying. We have observed that cylinders prepared in this way of lead-free brass tubing have never given a negative count rate beyond the statistical error when used on carbon derived from coal or oil. They would be expected to register negatively if the sample cylinders were contaminated, the point being that the inert carbon would absorb radiation from the brass. In addition, we have found Armco iron and pure copper sample cylinders to give the same count rate as the cleaned brass cylinders. We therefore believe that not over 0.1 or 0.2 count per minute of contamination exists on our set of sample cylinders and that it is possible to use Armco iron and pure copper as well as lead-free brass.

The statistical error of the count is taken as the square root of the total number of counts divided by the number of minutes during which they occurred. This gives the standard deviation a measure of error 1.5 times the probable error, and all of our results are quoted with this standard error derived solely from the count rate indicated. It has been interesting to observe that the scatter of repeated runs on different portions of a given sample and on recounts of a single portion of a given sample seems not to exceed the error due to the counting alone by any considerable factor. We therefore are inclined to believe that the use of longer counting periods would result in errors almost inversely proportional to the square root of the factor by which the counting time is increased. For example, if our present 48-hour counting interval, which gives us an error of ± 200 years for a sample of a certain age, should be increased by a factor of 4, we might be justified in assigning a ± 100-year error. Only further careful investigation can test this point and fully establish it. It does, however, seem likely that counting for periods even as long as a month with the consequent smaller errors might be worth while.

Since publication of the first edition, the techniques of measurement of the radiocarbon content of organic matter have been considerably improved. Among the improvements for those methods using solid carbon as the sample are (1) further reduction of the background by the use of a mercury shield, as proved by Kulp and Tryon;[5] (2) the ignition or baking of the carbon sample under conditions protecting it from radioactive contamination to reduce its specific area so that the chance of radioactive contamination during subsequent handling is reduced to a minimum, as accomplished by Rafter;[6] (3) an automatic sample changer, by Crane and McDaniel;[7] and (4) the introduction of a second counter into a given envelope so that two samples can be measured simultaneously, by Anderson et al.[8] With these improvements, the solid-carbon-sample techniques continue to be reliable and useful. It does seem to be clear, however, that some of the newer methods of gas counting, which have been developed during the last two or three years, have potentialities which exceed those of the solid-carbon counting methods. The scintillation counter also looks promising.[9]

Perhaps the most promising of the gaseous counting techniques is the acetylene method, since it has resulted in more dates than the other methods and is better established. It seems that the only real unexplored difficulty of the acetylene method is the possibility of explosion, and, since the record has been good to date, one is inclined to believe that this is not a serious hazard. In common with the other gaseous counting techniques, there are difficulties which are different from those of the solid method. Among these is, of course, the impossibility of routinely checking the background with the sample essentially in place. This has not proved, however, to be so serious a difficulty as one might have feared, and the gas counting methods look extremely promising on the whole. Acetylene is prepared essentially as described in the previous chapter as quoted from the publication of Suess.[10] Two groups have been involved independently in the development—a group at the United States Geological Survey in Washington, D.C., with Suess, and one at the

5. J. L. Kulp and L. E. Tryon, *Rev. Sci. Inst.*, **23**, 296 (1952).

6. T. A. Rafter, *New Zealand J. Sci. & Tech.*, **35**, 64 (1953).

7. H. R. Crane and E. W. McDaniel, *Science*, **116**, 342 (1952).

8. E. C. Anderson, H. Levi, and H. Tauber, *Science*, **118**, 6 (1953).

9. J. R. Arnold, *Science*, **119**, 155 (1954).

10. H. E. Suess, *Science*, **120**, 5 (1954).

British Museum, with Crathorn.[11] Suess describes the measurement in the following fashion. After noting that the shield is similar to that used with the solid-carbon counting techniques, he says that a linear amplifier is used for the amplification of the pulses from the counter, whose inside diameter is 7 cm. and whose volume is 1 liter, with a 0.002-inch diameter center wire made of stainless steel. The counter is surrounded by a mercury shield 1.5 cm. in thickness. The pulses taken from the linear amplifier are fed into an antico-incidence circuit where cancellation against the surrounding anti-coincidence counter shield of Geiger counters occurs. He says that a separate negative high-voltage supply keeps the counter case at a potential of 2000 volts with respect to ground and that the case is insulated by a Teflon sheet. The center wire attains a positive voltage of 3000 volts with respect to ground, so that the total voltage across the counter when filled with the acetylene to about 72 cm. of mercury pressure is some 5000 volts. The method has proved to be stable and reliable with respect to reproducibility, of background and reliability of the electronic equipment. There seems to be no doubt at all that the acetylene technique is established and that only further use can disclose any weaknesses. These, how-ever, cannot be serious. There may be points of some minor impor-tance in the observed fractionation of the isotopes during the incom-plete conversion of the sample to acetylene. It is also to be hoped that the explosion hazard will not increase.

Several groups, more or less independently, attacked the prob-lem of measuring carbon dioxide gas directly for its radiocarbon con-tent. This has been attractive because of the simplicity of the prepa-ration of this gas. In Holland, DeVries and Barendsen[12] were the first seriously to attack the problem of using carbon dioxide gas and to report success. Since their pioneering work, other groups have joined the development: in America, Brannon, Taggart, and Wil-liams, of the Humble Oil and Refining Company of Houston, Texas;[13] in New Zealand, Fergusson;[14] and, in Germany, Haxel

11. A. R. Crathorn, *Nature*, **172**, 632 (1953).

12. Hl. deVries and G. W. Barendsen, *Physica*, **18**, 652 (1952).

13. H. R. Brannon, M. S. Taggart, and M. Williams, private communication via Andover Conference on Radiocarbon Dating at R. S. Peabody Foundation, Phillips Academy, October 21–23, 1954.

14. G. J. Fergusson, private communication via Andover Conference on Radio-carbon Dating at R. S. Peabody Foundation, Phillips Academy, October 21–23, 1954.

in Heidelberg.[15] All these laboratories have attempted the use of carbon dioxide as a proportional counter gas. As we remark later, one other group at the University of Michigan, under H. R. Crane, is using it in the Geiger counter range. The essential difficulty in the use of carbon dioxide appears to have been established as a requirement of extreme purity. Apparently impurities of the order of parts per million will greatly reduce the multiplication factor for the electron discharge in carbon dioxide gas. Therefore it is necessary to use extreme methods of purification. The methods developed[16] utilize the absorption of the carbon dioxide on hot calcium oxide which has been previously pumped while hot. After the absorption, the material is pumped further, and impurities which are chemically distinguishable from carbon dioxide, of course, are removed or else are absorbed to form compounds of a different dissociation pressure from calcium carbonate. After the purification pumping, the material is heated from its pumping temperature of about 600° C. up to a temperature of about 800° C., when the carbon dioxide is released and stored for introduction into the counter. This purification procedure seems to have been shown to be adequate, so that reproducible multiplication factors can be obtained. Though the counter is by no means perfectly proportional, its performance is sufficiently satisfactory to enable one to use such extreme pressures as 10 atmospheres and counter voltages of 12,000 volts.[17] There seems to be little doubt that this technique, when pursued further, will establish a record rivaling that already established by the acetylene method, and it does seem likely that both of them will, perhaps, make the solid-carbon counting technique obsolete.

As mentioned above, Crane[18] uses carbon dioxide as a Geiger counter gas without the stringent purifications found necessary for its use as a proportional counter. The calcium carbonate precipitate, as described in a previous chapter, is acidified and the evolved

---

15. O. Haxel, private communication, May, 1954.

16. Hl. deVries and G. W. Barendsen, *Physica*, **18**, 652 (1952); H. R. Brannon, M. S. Taggart, and M. Williams, private communication, October 21–23, 1954; G. J. Fergusson, private communication, October 21–23, 1954.

17. H. R. Brannon, M. S. Taggart, and M. Williams, private communication, October 21–23, 1954.

18. H. R. Crane, private communication via Andover Conference on Radiocarbon Dating at R. S. Peabody Foundation, Phillips Academy, October 21–23, 1954.

carbon dioxide dried and passed into the counter. The carbon dioxide sample is mixed with a small amount of carbon disulfide at a pressure of about 1 mm. of mercury. The carbon disulfide has the function of masking the electron-capturing characteristics of the other impurities because of its abundance. It has the additional property of dissociating rather readily on reaching the high field near the positively charged wire and so raising the counter efficiency to nearly 100 per cent. The difficulty with this method of measuring the radiocarbon content of carbon dioxide is that the pulse time is 2 or 3 milliseconds, so that for larger counters the time required in coincidence cancellation of the pulses due to the cosmic-ray mesons becomes appreciable. For example, a 4-inch diameter counter would lose about 25 per cent of its counting time in this way, whereas a 5-inch or 6-inch counter would lose perhaps 50 per cent. Typical results quoted by Crane are: A 2.5-inch diameter counter with an effective length of 14 inches, less 0.5 inch or so at each end, has a background rate of 5 counts per minute and a rate of 10 counts per minute with modern carbon dioxide. A larger counter, with a 3.5-inch diameter, gives a background of 7 counts per minute and 15.5 counts per minute total with modern carbon dioxide, or a net of 8.5 counts per minute. Each pulse is quenched electrically. There is no real Geiger counter action, but the counter seems to operate very reliably and satisfactorily and holds considerable promise for the future.

CHAPTER VI

RADIOCARBON DATES[*]

THE dates obtained prior to the fall of 1954 by the radio-carbon technique are listed below. The number of runs is indicated by the number of dates listed. These runs were completely independent, involving separate portions of the original sample from which the carbon had been extracted independently, unless the dates are linked together with a brace. In this case, the results are those obtained by remeasurement of a given sample, usually in a different counter, and frequently involving re-extraction of the sample with acid. The standard counting time for a given run has been limited to 48 hours in order to accommodate the number of samples necessary to the over-all check of the method, which was the main purpose of this research. The errors given are standard deviations, consisting solely of the error of counting random events.

The archeological and geological significance of these results have been or will be discussed by the donors of the samples, collaborators, and the advisory committee in articles in appropriate journals.[1] We wish to express our gratitude to Frederick Johnson, Donald Collier, Richard Foster Flint, and Froelich Rainey, the members of the Committee on Carbon 14 of the American Anthropological Association and the Geological Society of America, for their indispensable direction and assistance throughout this research.

The numbering of the samples and the names we have used (which appear in parentheses when two names are given) are entirely our own and not those of the donors or collaborators. In many instances more appropriate names assigned by Mr. Johnson are given before the parentheses. The records on the samples are so extensive and so intimately tied to the sample names as well as to the numbers that we feel obliged to include our name as well as the number, though it may be misleading in many cases. The carbon for each of the samples listed is on file and available for check measurements, together in many instances with portions of the original materials.

---

[*] See Addendum to Chapter VI, p. x above.

1. See, e.g., *Radiocarbon Dating*, assembled by Frederick Johnson ("Society for American Archaeology Memoir," No. 8 [July, 1951]).

I. MESOPOTAMIA AND WESTERN ASIA
(*Principal collaborators:* R. J. BRAIDWOOD, T. JACOBSEN
RICHARD A. PARKER, AND SAUL WEINBERG)

A. EGYPT

Our No.	Sample	Age (Years)
C-1	*Zoser:* Acacia wood beam in excellent state of preservation from tomb of Zoser at Sakkara. Known age 4650 ± 75 years according to John Wilson. Submitted by Ambrose Lansing, Metropolitan Museum.	3699 ± 770 4234 ± 600 3991 ± 500 *Av. 3979 ± 350*
C-12	*Sneferu:* Cypress beam from tomb of Sneferu at Meydum. Known age 4575 ± 75 according to John Wilson. Submitted by Froelich Rainey, University of Pennsylvania Museum.	4721 ± 500 4186 ± 500 5548 ± 500 4817 ± 240 *Av. 4802 ± 210*
C-81	*Sesostris:* Wood from deck of funerary ship from tomb of Sesostris III. Known age 3750 according to John Wilson. Submitted by Colonel C. C. Gregg, Chicago Natural History Museum.	3845 ± 400 3407 ± 500 3642 ± 310 *Av. 3621 ± 180*
C-62	*Ptolemy:* Wood from mummiform coffin from Egyptian Ptolemaic period. Known age 2280 according to John Wilson. Submitted by John Wilson and Watson Boyes, Oriental Institute, University of Chicago.	2190 ± 450
C-267	*Hemaka:* Slab of wood from roof beam of tomb of Vizier Hemaka, contemporaneous with King Udimu, First Dynasty, at Sakkara. Accepted age 4700–5100 according to R. J. Braidwood. Sample submitted by W. B. Emery, % British Embassy, Cairo.	{ 4803 ± 260 { 4961 ± 240 *Av. 4883 ± 20*
C-463	*Middle Predynastic (Predynastic):* Charcoal from point "A-15" of the house floors (*fonds de cabanes*) at El Omari near Cairo, Egypt. A typological assessment of the position of El Omari would be *ca.* midway between the time of the Upper K pits of the Fayum (Nos. C-457, C-550, and C-551) and Hemaka (No. C-267). Submitted by Fernand de Bono, Service des Antiquités de l'Égypte, Cairo.	5256 ± 230
C-457	*Fayum A (Upper K):* Wheat and barley grain uncarbonized with no preservatives added, from Upper K Pit 13 of the Fayum A material as described in *The Desert Fayum* by Gertrude Caton-Thompson. Submitted by Miss Caton-Thompson of Cambridge and Mrs. Elise Baumgartel of the Museum of the University of Manchester.	{ 6054 ± 330 { 6136 ± 320 *Av. 6095 ± 250*
C-550 C-551	*Fayum A (Upper K):* Wheat and barley grain from Upper K Pit 59, Jar 3, and another of the Upper K pits (number lost) of the Fayum A material as de-	6391 ± 180

Our No.	Sample	Age (Years)

scribed in *The Desert Fayum*. Submitted by Miss Caton-Thompson and Mrs. Elise Baumgartel.

C-753
C-754
   Shaheinab near Khartoum, Sudan: This ancient site may be the clue as to whether some elements in Egyptian civilization came from Africa northward. The site is about 1200 miles from the Egyptian Fayum (Nos. C-457, C-550, C-551—the Egyptian granaries, which dated 6240 years); and the archeological connection with the Fayum Neolithic is close. Collected in 1949 by A. J. Arkell, Department of Egyptology, University College, London. Submitted by R. J. Braidwood, Oriental Institute, University of Chicago.

   C-753   *Shaheinab Charcoal:* Two lots, one marked "N80, 20–40" and the other "066(5)."   5060 ± 450

   C-754   *Shaheinab Shell:* Bivalve shells from Shaheinab, apparently in fairly unaltered condition.   5446 ± 380

C-810   *Nagada (Predynastic Hair I):* Human hair weighing about 3 ounces, found in a cemetery at Nagada in southern Egypt in 1896. This material belongs to Predynastic Egypt, that is, is older than about 5000 years. The British archeologist W. Flinders Petrie constructed a scheme of what he called "Sequence Dates," on the basis of changing pottery styles, dividing the Predynastic period of Egypt into eighty Sequence Dates. This sample consisted about half of material from Grave 1592 with a Sequence Date of 34; one-quarter from Grave 1487 with a Sequence Date of 38; and the rest from Graves 1562 (Sequence Date 35) and 1816 (Sequence Date 35). Submitted by Miss Margaret Armit, Department of Archaeology and Ethnology, Cambridge University, England.   5744 ± 300

C-811   *Nagada (Predynastic Hair II):* Human hair weighing about ⅔ ounce found in a cemetery at Nagada in southern Egypt in 1896. This material belongs to Predynastic Egypt, and it is older than about 5000 years. The British archeologist W. Flinders Petrie constructed a scheme of what he called "Sequence Dates" on the basis of changing pottery styles, dividing the Predynastic period into eighty Sequence Dates. About one-third of this sample consisted of material from Grave 1401 (Sequence Date 42), one-third from Grave 1863 (Sequence Date 46), one-third from Grave 1410 (Sequence Dates 36–44), and a small amount (½ gram) from Grave 1729 (Se-   5619 ± 280

Our No.	Sample	Age (Years)

quence Date 40). These samples, as well as C-810, C-812, C-813, and C-814, all came from Petrie's excavations at Nagada. They were taken from the Flinders Petrie Collection at University College. Submitted by Margaret Armit.

C-812   *Nagada II (Predynastic Hair III)*: Human hair and skin from Grave T.56, dated by Elise Baumgartel generally as "Nagada II." Weight 45.5 grams, including about 20 grams of human skin. Submitted by Margaret Armit. 5020 ± 290

C-813   *Nagada II (Predynastic Hair IV)*: Twenty grams of hair from Grave 733 (Sequence Dates 58–67) and 5 grams of hair from Grave 1349 (Sequence Dates 58–67). Both portions were used. Submitted by Margaret Armit. 4720 ± 310

C-814   *Nagada (Predynastic Skin)*: Human skin weighing about 2 ounces, found in a cemetery at Nagada in southern Egypt in 1896, as in the case of No. C-810. This material came from Grave 1609 (Sequence Dates 34–38). Submitted by Margaret Armit. 5577 ± 300

B. TURKEY

C-115   *Alishar III (Alishar)*: Wood from the foundation cribbing for a fortification wall in Square 0–10 in levels assigned to Period III, "Early Bronze Age," in the mound at Alishar Huyuh by the excavator, H. H. von der Osten. Reference: "Oriental Institute Publications," **28**, 209–10; Figure 207. Submitted by R. J. Braidwood. 3650 ± 350
 2823 ± 350
 Av. 3212 ± 250

C-183   *Alishar Chalcolithic:* Wood from Level 14 in the central depth cut Square L–14, Alishar Huyuh. The excavators counted Levels 19 through 13 as "Chalcolithic." Reference: "Oriental Institute Publications," Vol. **28**. Submitted by R. J. Braidwood. 4519 ± 250

C. IRAQ

C-113   *Jarmo:* Land-snail shells fairly well preserved from the basal Levels 7 and 8 at Jarmo. Earliest village material in western Asia. The basal levels are pre-ceramic. Excavated and submitted by R. J. Braidwood. 6707 ± 320

C-742   *Jarmo, Iraq (Jarmo II)*: Jarmo is an early village site in the *liwa* of Kirkuk, Iraq, midway between the towns of Kirkuk and Sulimaniyah. This site is early Neolithic and exhibits the earliest traces of an established food-producing village economy in the 6606 ± 330

"nuclear" Near East. Only the upper third of the
site yielded portable pottery, but there was a well-
established architectural manifestation throughout
the 7.10 meters of depth and traces of about a dozen
"floors" or building renovations. An excavation labeled "I" was made clear to virgin soil near one edge
of the mound. Eight floors were found. A second excavation, labeled "II," was made at the highest point.
This went down 4 meters through the sixth floor,
which is still 3.2 meters above virgin soil. The sixth
floor of II is equivalent to the third floor of I, and the
second floor of II is equivalent to the first floor of I.
The earlier Jarmo sample (No. C-113), consisting of
shell, came from the seventh floor of I. It dated at
6707 ± 320 years. The present sample, consisting of
flecks of charcoal collected by the pickmen as they
cleared the levels, came from the same spot as the
earlier shell sample. Especially for the deep floors,
such as the seventh, the character of the fine-grained
touf debris and of the *touf* walls themselves was such
as to give absolute confidence in the undisturbed
nature of the locality. Collected and submitted by
R. J. Braidwood.

C-743   *Jarmo, Iraq (Jarmo III)*: Charcoal from the fifth   6695 ± 360
        floor of excavation II (see Nos. C-742 and C-113).
        Submitted by R. J. Braidwood.

C-744   *Jarmo (Jarmo IV)*: Jarmo is an early village site in the   5266 ± 450
        liwa of Kirkuk, Iraq, midway between the towns of
        Kirkuk and Sulimaniyah. This site is early Neolithic
        and exhibits the earliest traces of an established food-
        producing village economy in the "nuclear" Near
        East. Only the upper third of the site yielded portable
        pottery, but there was a well-established architectur-
        al manifestation throughout the 7.10 meters of depth,
        and there were traces of about a dozen "floors" or
        building renovations. An excavation labeled "I" was
        made clear to virgin soil near one edge of the mound.
        A second excavation, labeled "II," was made from
        the highest point. This went down 4 meters through
        the sixth floor, which is still 3.2 meters above virgin
        soil. The sixth floor of II is equivalent to the third
        floor of I, and the second floor of II is equivalent to
        the first floor of I. The earlier Jarmo sample (No.
        C-113), consisting of shell, came from the seventh
        floor of I. It dated 6707 ± 320 years. The present
        sample, consisting of flecks of charcoal collected by
        the pickmen as they cleared the levels, came from

Our
No.   Sample   Age (Years)

J–II—2 and J–II—2d floor. This material was high
in the mound and near the surface. Collected and submitted by R. J. Braidwood.

C-752 *Nippur (Nippur I, II, III)*: In the case of this sample   3945 ± 106
a serious attempt was made to test the limit of sensi-
tivity of the radiocarbon dating method. An important subject, the time of Hammurabi of Babylon,
was selected, and the sample, which consisted of a
charcoal beam from the roof of a house definitely
fixed in the Hammurabian calendar, was divided into
three equal portions and each portion measured as a
separate individual for nearly 1 month of steady
counting time. The total time of 3 months spent in
this investigation we hope has served to establish the
true limiting accuracy of the method as now developed.

The dating of the time of Hammurabi of Babylon
is approached by dating the associated kings Ibi-Sin
and Shu-Sin, who lived about 250 years before Hammurabi, but at a time accurately known on the Babylonian calendar. Hence a date for Ibi-Sin or Shu-
Sin correspondingly fixes the date of accession of
Hammurabi. The material used was charcoal which
was excavated in Nippur by Donald E. McCown,
of the Oriental Institute, University of Chicago,
in March, 1950, at Area TB, Locus 195, Level
IV, Floor 2. The charcoal came from a roof beam of
a house of Level IV, Floor 2. The archeological situation of dated tablets makes it highly probable that
this building was constructed not later than Year 3 of
Ibi-Sin or earlier than Year 1 of Shu-Sin (a range of
12 years).

The point at issue chronologically is that, while
the Mesopotamian king list on the Babylonian calendar is internally reliable, it is in itself a floating
chronology, Hence, for example, the dates for the accession of Hammurabi of Babylon as currently given
by various authors cover a range of at least 350 years.
The date is thought to be important historically not
only for strictly Mesopotamian problems but for the
whole interwoven fabric of historic interrelationships
of western Asia and Egypt in the early part of the
second millennium B.C.

The results for the three portions of charcoal were
4.029 ± 0.05, 4.085 ± 0.07, and 4.156 ± 0.13 counts per
minute. Modern wood gives 6.68 counts per minute.
The question one considers first is whether the three

determinations agree within the counting errors, for
the errors indicated above are calculated solely on
the basis of the square root of the total number of
counts taken, this being the standard deviation
within which the true value has a two-thirds probability of being found. It certainly is a minimum error.
These are the errors quoted above. It does seem that
the three determinations do agree within their individual counting errors and that therefore the samples
are uncontaminated by extraneous radioactivity. If
one were certain that the errors lay principally in the
counting, the mean of the three determinations
should be taken by using the inverse square of the
counting errors as weighting factors. The weighted
average taken in this way is 4.060 ± 0.042, for an age
of 4004 years ± 106 years, or 2052 ± 106 B.C. It is
probably better, however, to take the arithmetical
average, since there are undoubtedly other errors
than the counting errors. The arithmetical average
is 4.090 ± 0.04. In striking this average, we use the
same calculation for the error used for the weighted
average, since the errors quoted throughout are determined solely by the counting error. The latter
mean corresponds to an age of 3945 ± 106 years, or
1993 ± 106 B.C. The error 0.04 corresponds to 80
years in itself, but an estimated 0.54 per cent error
in the half-life of radiocarbon and 0.67 per cent in
the assay of modern wood must be included. Combining, we obtain 106 years. Our conclusion is that
this sample of charcoal came from wood which was
cut or ceased to live about 3945 years ago. More
definitely, we conclude that for two chances out of
three it died between 2100 and 1887 B.C. and that for
nineteen chances out of twenty it died between 2205
and 1781 B.C. Since the allowable range from other
evidence seems to be 2374–1975 B.C., we conclude that
the younger of the possible calendars is strongly
favored by the radiocarbon dating. The odds against
a result 130 years higher than the mean are about
nine to one. Sample submitted by Donald E. Mc-
Cown, Oriental Institute, University of Chicago.

C-817   *Tepe Gawra Ash (Tepe Gawra)*: The sample of ash
was taken from the trench face of the Tepe Gawra
site in the spring of 1951 at a level 2 meters above
the apparent greatest depth in the low central operation. A fragmentary Ubaid painted jar was in contact with the hearth which yielded this ash (cf.

$\begin{cases} 5552 \pm 350 \\ 5100 \pm 800 \end{cases}$
Av. 5400 ± 325

Our No.	Sample	Age (Years)

Tobler, *Excavations at Tepe Gawra*, Vol. **2**, Pls. XVII–XIX). Level 19 is the deepest in the area; a point 2 meters above this would fall above the floor of Level 18, but certainly not higher than Level 17. It is certain that the sample came from between Floors 17 and 18.

A date for this level would give the point at which the Ubaid period took on its first flourish in northern Iraq. This is of importance, because the change involved was one from peasant villages to market towns with temples; it would lead to new understanding of the general rate of acceleration of cultural growth at a critical point. Collected and submitted by Mr. and Mrs. R. J. Braidwood.

C-818 *Hazer Merd:* Charcoal ash sample from the "Mousterian" level of the Hazer Merd cave in Sulimaniyah, Iraq. This cave was excavated by Miss Dorothy Garrod in 1928 (*Bull. Am. School Prehist. Research*, **6**, 24–37 [1930]). The sample was collected by Mrs. R. J. Braidwood and Bruce Howe in April, 1951, from Layer C of the exposed trench face which still showed the dark ash lines shown in Miss Garrod's published section. One of these ash lines was cleaned and the sample taken from it. Submitted by R. J. Braidwood.

Older than 25,000

D. SYRIA

C-72 *Tayinat:* Wood from the floor of a central room (I–J—1st) in a large Hilani ("palace") of the "Syro-Hittite" period in the city of Tayinat in northwest Syria. Known age 2625 ± 50 years according to R. J. Braidwood. Submitted by R. J. Braidwood.

2696 ± 270
2648 ± 270
2239 ± 270
Av. 2531 ± 150

E. IRAN

C-492
C-547
C-525
C-574
C-524
C-494
C-495
C-523
Belt Cave (Ghar-i-Kamarband): Five miles west of Behshahr at the southeast corner of the Caspian Sea; stratified cultural deposit 4.05 meters thick containing from, bottom to top, Mesolithic, late Mesolithic, Neolithic, late Neolithic, and Bronze Age materials. The samples were burned bone which were treated by dissolving in hydrochloric acid to separate the charred carbon, which was measured. This material was collected and submitted by Carleton S. Coon, University of Pennsylvania Museum. Five samples were measured:

C-492 Lowest gray soil with Mesolithic artifacts
C-547 3.00–4.05 meters (Levels 21–28).

8004 ± 415

Our No.		Sample	Age (Years)
C-525		Supposedly from the same levels as No. C-574. Comment: looks intrusive or altered.	$\begin{cases} 1130 \pm 300 \\ 1260 \pm 430 \end{cases}$
C-574		Zone containing Upper Mesolithic artifacts, 1.25–2.15 meters deep (Layers 15 and 16).	8545 ± 500
C-524		Mesolithic-Neolithic transition at 1.25–1.40 meters (Layer 10).	$10,560 \pm 610$
C-494 C-495 C-523		Zone containing flint blades of pottery sherds of Neolithic type.	8085 ± 720

F. PALESTINE

C-576 *Bible:* Dead Sea scrolls. Book of Isaiah. Linen wrappings used. Found in cave near Ain Fashkha in Palestine by Père de Vaux (OP) under supervision by G. Lankester Harding, curator of Department of Antiquities of the Jordan Government. Thought to be first or second century B.C. Brought for test by James L. Kelso at suggestion of Ovid R. Sellers and with permission of Mr. Harding. Submitted directly by C. H. Kraeling, Oriental Institute, University of Chicago. 1917 ± 200

C-919 *Beer-Sheba (Beer-Sheba):* Charcoal from the lowest of three strata of a "chalcolithic" site at Khirbet el-Bitar, near Beer-Sheba, in Israel. The two overlying strata both contained architecture, and there is no hint of intrusion. The sample was associated with potsherds, and Ben-Dor writes that "this culture is supposed to be akin to the so-called 'Ghassulian' culture of eastern Palestine." The "Ghassulian" is an assemblage for which dates have been assigned which vary over several thousand years. It would be a useful check point not only for our understanding of Palestine but also in terms of the general comparative archeology of the Near East. Submitted by R. J. Braidwood. 7420 ± 520

G. AFGHANISTAN

C-815 *Mundigak (Afghanistan Bronze Age):* Charcoal from the prehistoric site of Mundigak in the province of Kandahar, excavated by the expedition headed by M. J. M. Casal. Came from Layer 23, which is certainly at the very beginning of the Bronze Age and possibly a little earlier. The Afghanistan chronology is unknown prior to the Hellenistic contact (Alexander the Great). The painted pottery of the basal levels is similar to the late prehistoric pottery of Iran in a general way. A date for this material would add 4720 ± 270 4439 ± 280 *Av. 4580 ± 200*

Our No.	Sample	Age (Years)

to the general understanding of the area itself, which is otherwise undatable, and to a better grasp of Near East–Indus Valley relationships, which will probably be cleared up best by understanding the intervening regions of Baluchistan and Afghanistan. Submitted by Daniel Schlumberger, director of the French Archaeological Expedition in Afghanistan, Kabul, Afghanistan.

H. Lebanon

C-819 *Byblos:* Wood from a house in the ancient Lebanese city of Byblos. This sample comes from a level identified as "First Urban Installation" of Byblos, which is to be taken as being roughly equivalent to what is called the "Early Bronze Age I" in Palestine, which should be about the time of the late Predynastic–early Dynasty I of Egypt. The port of Byblos was probably an important trading center at that time. There is evidence of trade contact between Egypt and Syria. This material is expected to be roughly contemporaneous with No. C-627, Hemaka, which dated 4883 ± 200. Submitted by M. A. Dunand, French Embassy, Beirut, Lebanan, through R. J. Braidwood.
5317 ± 300

II. WESTERN EUROPE

(*Principal collaborators:* H. L. Movius, Jr., E. S. Deevey, Jr., and R. F. Flint)

A. France

C-406 *Lascaux:* Charcoal from the Lascaux cave near Montignac northeast of Les Eyzies in the Dordogne. This cave has the remarkable paintings The charcoal was taken from the occupation level in the northwestern portion of the cave by Abbé H. Breuil and M. Severin Blanc in 1949. Submitted by H. L. Movius, Jr., Harvard University.
$15,516 \pm 900$

C-577 *France:* Material from a late Upper Paleolithic (Magdalenian) occupation layer overlain by 1.5–2.0 meters of rock fall. Collected in and around a hearth which measured 60 cm. in diameter and 10 cm. in thickness at the center. Found at La Garenne, St.-Marcel (Indre), France. This sample consisted of 1500 grams of burned bone from which sufficient organic material was obtained by acid dissolution of the bone. Submitted by Dr. J. Allain, 34, Avenue Thabaud-Bois-
$11,109 \pm 480$

Our No.	Sample	Age (Years)
	lareine, Neuvy-St.-Sépulchre (Indre), France, through H. L. Movius, Jr.	
C-578	*France II:* Same as No. C-577, except that it consisted of an ashy material with sand, charcoal, and burned bones.	15,847 ± 1200
C-579	*France III:* Same as Nos. C-577 and C-578, except found outside the hearth but in same horizon. Burned bone.	12,986 ± 560
C-588	*Lake Bourget:* Lake Bourget wood and peat samples taken along road between Chambéry and Grenoble in southeastern France. Should be interglacial or interstadial. This sample was wood from 2 inches above base of Level 3d, the lowest lignite bed in the exposure between La Flachère and La Brussère (Isère). Donor's sample No. 1. Submitted by H. L. Movius, Jr.	At least 21,000
C-595	*Geneva:* Wood from peat bed in Dranse Valley east of Geneva and south of Lake Geneva in France rather than Switzerland. Submitted by H. L. Movius, Jr.	At least 19,000

B. GERMANY

Our No.	Sample	Age (Years)
C-337	*German Alleröd:* Peat with birch remains from Pollen Zone IIb, the younger Alleröd, from Wallensen im Hils, northwestern Germany. Submitted by F. Firbas, Göttingen.	11,044 ± 500
C-450	*Grenz Horizant Peat (Overbeck Peat):* Peat (Grenz Horizant) from an accurately dated (1500–2700 years) dry period extending throughout northern Europe and associated with archeological remains. This sample was taken carefully from 0 to 2 cm. below the dry horizon at Melhack, Germany. Submitted by F. Overbeck, University of Bonn.	$\begin{cases} 1446 \pm 250 \\ 1452 \pm 290 \end{cases}$ *Av. 1449 ± 200*
C-449	*Grenz Horizant Peat (Overbeck Top):* Peat from 0 to 2 cm. above the dry horizon described in No. C-450. Submitted by F. Overbeck.	1129 ± 115

C. DENMARK

Our No.	Sample	Age (Years)
C-432	*Danish Boreal (Danish Boreal II):* Pine cones from Denmark (Seeland, Aamosen; Ogaarde-K, PØ 1949). They are from Pollen Zone V thought to be 8500 years old. Submitted by J. Troels-Smith, National Museum, Copenhagen.	7583 ± 380
C-433	*Danish Boreal (Boreal IV):* Hazelnuts from Denmark (Seeland, Aamosen; Kildegaard-K, Ul. Ø, House 1). The nuts are from one single summer dwelling, be-	$\begin{cases} 9935 \pm 440 \\ 9927 \pm 830 \end{cases}$ *Av. 9931 ± 350*

Our No.	Sample	Age (Years)

longing to the late boreal age, Pollen Zone VI, thought to be about 8000 years old. Submitted by J. Troels-Smith.

C-434 *Danish Boreal (Danish Boreal III)*: Charcoal from the same summer house as No. C-433. Expected age about 8000 years. Submitted by J. Troels-Smith. — 8631 ± 540

C-435 *Danish Boreal (Danish House)*: Birchwood from the same area as Nos. C-433 and C-434. From House 2. Probably a few years younger than House 1. Submitted by J. Troels-Smith. Comment: Seems to agree with No. C-433 and possibly No. C-434, giving a general mean of 9479 ± 280 years. — 9425 ± 470

D. IRELAND

C-358 *Irish Boreal (Boreal II)*: Peat from Clonsast, County Offaly, Ireland. Late Boreal Zone VIc. Should be later than Danish No. C-432 and earlier than English No. C-343. Donor's sample No. I-D. Submitted by G. F. Mitchell, Trinity College, Dublin. — 5824 ± 300

C-355 *Irish Mud:* Lake mud from Knocknacran, County Monaghan, Ireland. Late Glacial, Pollen Zone II. Donor's sample No. I-A. Submitted by G. F. Mitchell. — 11,310 ± 720

C-356 *Irish Postglacial:* Lake mud, Lagore, County Meath. Early Postglacial, Zone IV. Donor's sample No. I-B. Submitted by G. F. Mitchell. — 11,787 ± 700

C-877 *Irish Cooking Place (Irish I)*: Samples of oak wood (*Quercus*) from an ancient Irish cooking place at Killeens, County Cork. This is site No. 1. Submitted by M. J. O'Kelly, Cork Publick Museum, Fitzerald Park, Cork, and Eamon de Valera, Dublin. — 3506 ± 230

C-878 *Irish Cooking Place (Irish II)*: Oak wood as from an ancient Irish cooking place at Killeens, site No. 2. Submitted by M. J. O'Kelly and Eamon de Valera. — 3713 + 270

E. ENGLAND

C-461 *Beeswax:* Lump of beeswax associated with a smith's hoard of late Bronze Age objects of estimated 2500–3000 years age. Question is whether it is part of hoard or not. Submitted by J. W. Brailsford, British Museum. Comment: Is not part of hoard; it is younger. — { 712 ± 200 / 926 ± 230 / *Av. 819 ± 160* }

C-347 *Shapwick (Shapwick Peat)*: Modified humified peat (Sphagnum-Calluna) from mid-Iron Age to Romano- — { 3099 ± 250 / 3520 ± 300 }

Our No.	Sample	Age (Years)
	British period from Shapwick Heath, Somerset. Pollen Zone VIII. Upper Oligotrophic layer; decay pool wood; cf. S.H.6. Submitted by H. Godwin, Cambridge, England.	Av. 3310 ±200
C-343	*Shapwick (Shapwick Atlantic)*: Humified Sphagnum-Calluna peat of Neolithic age, early Pollen Zone VII, taken from 6 feet 8 inches to 7 feet at base of old peat at Dewar's track excavation. Submitted by H. Godwin.	6044 ±380
C-462	*English Neolithic (Mesolithic)*: Piece of charred wood from the lakeside settlement at Ehenside Tarn, Cumberland. Neolithic "A" material. Conventional dating is 4000 years (cf. *Archaeologia*, **44**, 280). One of rare cases in England where organic material has been preserved in association with characteristic Neolithic material. Submitted by J. W. Brailsford.	4964 ±300
C-353	*Starr Carr:* Wooden platform from Mesolithic site at Lake Pickering, Starr Carr, Yorkshire. Pollen Zone IV. Submitted by H. Godwin.	10,167 ±560 8808 ±490 Av. 9488 ±350
C-340	*Postglacial (Postglacial I)*: Peat from Hawks Tor, Cornwall. Pollen Zone IV, early Postglacial. Collected from 7 feet to 7 feet 4 inches at Site 1 at base of upper peat. Submitted by H. Godwin.	{ 8011 ±400 { 8540 ±780 Av. 8275 ±350
C-349	*Hockham Mere, England (English Alleröd)*: Calcareous silty neckron mud from 790 to 825 cm. at D.B. 5, Hockham Mere, Norfolk. Late Glacial, Pollen Zones II and III. Submitted by H. Godwin.	{ 6619 ±380 { 6491 ±420 Av. 6555 ±280
C-444	*Neasham, England (Godwin)*: Lake mud from Neasham near Darlington in the Extreme north of England. Pollen Zone II, correlated directly with last glacial stage. Submitted by H. Godwin.	10,851 ±630
C-341	*Hawks Tor, England (Alleröd I)*: Peat from Hawks Tor, Cornwall. Late Glacial, Pollen Zone II, 9 feet to 9 feet 4 inches at Site 1, middle of lower peat. Submitted by H. Godwin.	9861 ±500
C-479	*Ponders End:* Plant debris from Lea Valley Arctic Bed north of London at Ponders End. Glacial stage associated with mammoth, lemming, and arctic plants. Submitted by H. Godwin.	Older than 20,000
C-480	*Cambridge, England (Cambridge Interglacial)*: Oak wood debris from Histon Road, Cambridge. Middle of last interglacial, time of maximum extension of the Eem Sea. Submitted by H. Godwin.	At least 17,000
C-602	*Stonehenge:* Charcoal sample from Stonehenge, Wiltshire, England. Taken from Hole 32 of a series of	3798 ±275

holes that are believed to have been used for some
sort of ritual. These holes belong to the first phase of
the monument and are considered to be late Neolithic. Submitted by Professor Stuart Piggott, University of Edinburgh.

F. NETHERLANDS

C-627   *Dutch Prehistoric:* Charcoal and wood samples cover-
C-623   ing a considerable range in the chronologic column
C-621   of the Netherlands beginning in the Mesolithic (No.
        C-627). Submitted by A. E. van Giffen, director,
        Biological-Archaeological Institute, Groningen.

  C-627   *Dutch I:* Charcoal from Mesolithic site in the   7965 ± 370
          Netherlands. Donor's label: "Haule I Fr.
          Mesolithic, Netherlands, *ca.* 5000 B.C." Do-
          nor's sample No. A.

  C-623   *Dutch Bronze Age:* Charcoal from Province of   2523 ± 200
          Drente, thought to be of Bronze Age. Do-   2602 ± 290
          nor's label: "Oudemolen, Comm. Vries, Prov.   *Av. 2562 ± 175*
          Drenthe,   Tumulus   3.   2-period-barrow.
          Bronze Age." Donor's sample No. 15.

  C-621   *Groningen:* Wood from round church at St.   2222 ± 200
          Walburg in tower of Groningen. Piece of
          wooden post. Earliest ecclesiastical con-
          struction at St. Walburg can be dated to the
          third century A.D. at the latest. Possibly some
          buildings existed on this site as early as the
          second century; it is important to know
          whether such structural features are actually
          associated with early churches in the Nether-
          lands.

G. ICELAND

C-749   *History of the Geomagnetic Field, Reykjavik, Iceland*   5300 ± 340
        (*Iceland Peat*): The direction of the earth's magnetic
        field is recorded by solidifying lavas, as of the time
        of solidification, by the permanent polarization of
        the lava. Near Ellidhaá Bridge, Reykjavik, a lava
        flow occurs with polarization roughly parallel to the
        present geomagnetic field. It happened to flow over
        postglacial peat, which constitutes the sample. Its
        date correlates directly with that of the flow. Sub-
        mitted by B. C. Browne and J. Hospers, Department
        of Geodesy and Geophysics, Cambridge University,
        England.

III. UNITED STATES AND CANADA

(*Principal collaborators:* E. S. DEEVEY, JR., R. F. FLINT, J. B. GRIFFIN
R. F. HEIZER, F. JOHNSON, F. H. H. ROBERTS, AND W. S. WEBB)

A. NEW ENGLAND AND CANADA

Our No.	Sample	Age (Years)
C-417	*Boylston Street Fishweir (Fishweir I)*: Peat from Boylston Street Fishweir site. Lower peat underlying the fishweir. Presumably the fishweir should be younger (cf. *The Boylston Street Fishweir II* ["Papers of the Peabody Foundation," Vol. **4**, No. 1], pp. 60, 65, 68). Submitted by E. S. Barghoorn, Biological Laboratories, Harvard University.	5717 ± 500
C-418	*Boylston Street Fishweir (Fishweir II)*: Fragment of coniferous wood from marine silt overlying the lower peat and the fishweir (cf. No. C-417). Submitted by E. S. Barghoorn.	3851 ± 390
C-36 C-37 C-38 C-39	*Upper Linsley Pond (Deevey Series)*: Pond mud samples from Upper Linsley Pond, Connecticut (cf. E. S. Deevey, Jr., *Am. J. Sci.*, **241**, 717–52 [1943]). Samples were taken by boring through ice in center of pond. Collected and submitted by E. S. Deevey, Jr., Osborne Zoological Laboratory, Yale University.	

Sample	Depth (Meters)	Pollen Zone	
C-36	5.5	C3	876 ± 250
C-37	8.05	C2	1800 ± 500
C-38	9.15	C1–C2	5159 ± 350
C-39	11.65	C1–B	8323 ± 400

Our No.	Sample	
C-119 C-120 C-121 C-122	*Upper Linsley Pond (Linsley Series)*: Pond mud samples from Upper Linsley Pond, Connecticut. These were taken from the edge of the pond (cf. Nos. C-36–C-39). Collected and submitted by E. S. Deevey, Jr.	

Sample	Depth (Meters)	Pollen Zone	
C-119	4.65	C2	2141 ± 250
C-120	6.65	C1–C2	5305 ± 250
C-121	8.65	C1	Heterogeneous: 6911 and 4088 ± 250
C-122	10.15	B	6668 ± 250

Comment: Appears mixing is involved.

C-478	*Upper Linsley Pond (Linsley V)*: Peat from Upper Linsley Pond, Connecticut. Taken at 10.55 meters with large sampler. Pollen date is early to middle C-1.	8794 ± 550

Our No.	Sample	Age (Years)
	Pine zone is at 11.90 meters. Collected and submitted by E. S. Deevey, Jr.	
C-335	*Maine Boreal (Boreal I)*: Peat from 6.0 meters in Plissey Pond, Maine. Very top of Pine Zone B. Submitted by E. S. Deevey, Jr.	5962 ± 320
C-606	*Waterton, Canada:* Western Alberta, Canada, glacial forest bed in northwest quarter, Sec. 8, T. 2 R. 29 at Waterton (cf. Waterton Lakes topographic map). Stratigraphy: Top soil 1 foot; gravel 12 feet; lacustrine clay 0.5 foot; gravel 2 feet; sandy silt with invertebrate fossils 2 feet; forest bed 2 feet; dark-brown Kewatin drift 9 feet. This sample was wood. L. R. Wilson, University of Massachusetts, says it is black and white spruce. The ecology is similar to that at edge of tundra now. Submitted by C. L. Horberg, Department of Geology, University of Chicago.	3261 ± 250
C-607	*Waterton Peat:* Same as No. C-606, except peat instead of spruce wood.	3327 ± 320
C-608	*Burley Site, Lake Huron:* Charcoal from Occupational Horizon No. 1 from the Burley site, located on the northern terrace, formerly mouth of the Ausable River, about 1 mile from Lake Huron. This was an old Indian dwelling site. The profile is: (*a*) sand below the 12-foot level above the lake; (*b*) Occupational Horizon No. 1, consisting of dark sand of the most ancient occupational level (the charcoal, which was taken from this level, lies between the 12- and 14-foot elevations); (*c*) stratified alluvial sand with shells of fresh-water snails up to 15–17 feet; (*d*) second occupational level (No. 2), 6 inches to 1 foot thick; (*e*) light-gray sand 6 inches to 1 foot thick; (*f*) dark sand of the most recent occupational horizon (No. 3); (*g*) top cover of windblown sand, 1–2 feet thick, 18–20 feet above the present lake level. It is believed that this may date from the early one-outlet stage of the Nipissing Great Lakes. Collected by W. Jury, 1950. Submitted by A. Dreimanis, University of Western Ontario, London.	2619 ± 220
C-809	*Titicut Site (Titicut)*: Charcoal from a hearth from the lowest level at the Titicut site, Bridgewater, Massachusetts. This was a hearth from the lowest level, found 3 feet below the surface of the ground. It is composed of pieces of charcoal, black sandy soil, and pebbles. The hearth was covered by a thin layer of brownish fine sand that was overlain by a layer of gravel and fine white sand about 8	$\begin{cases} 4139 \pm 260 \\ 5750 \pm 720 \end{cases}$ *Av. 4500 ± 300*

inches thick. Above this there was a layer of yellow soil about 18 inches thick. Humus, the uppermost layer, covered the whole deposit. There was
no sign of disturbance or occupation in the layers
over the hearth. The distribution of the pebbles
and the soil indicated that the layers called "yellow
soil" and "gravel and fine white sand" had been deposited upon the hearth by natural movement of
materials. The building and use of the hearth ante-
dated this movement. The present hypothesis concerning this situation is that the soil layers were
moved over the hearth by congeliturbation during a
period when the climate was colder than at present.
Continuing geologic investigations may modify this
hypothesis.

The hearth is covered by a deposit of natural origin. Various similar deposits found on this site and
also a number of artifacts excavated from analogous
locations are evidence of occupation previous to the
movement of the materials. A date on the charcoal
will contribute to our knowledge of the age of the
occupation and the time when the geologic event responsible for the movement of the materials took
place. It is known that root hairs penetrate the pores
of the charcoal. Collected October 16, 1949, by J.
Hartshorn, Kirk Bryan, and Frederick Johnson.
Submitted by Frederick Johnson, R. S. Peabody
Foundation, Andover, Massachusetts.

B. NEW YORK STATE

C-191   *Frontenac Island* (*Frontenac*): Charcoal from hearth   4930 ± 260
in deepest refuse levels (Trench 4, Section 4), Fronte-
nac Island site. Collected in 1939, Lamoka Focus,
Archaic Period (revised terminology 1950) (cf.
Ritchie, 1945). From collections of Rochester Museum of Arts and Sciences. Submitted through W. A.
Ritchie, New York State Museum.

C-192   *Oberlander 2* (*Point Peninsula*): Charcoal from crema-   { 2817 ± 270
tion (Burial 6) on the Oberlander component No. 2   { 3080 ± 200
at Brewerton, Oswego County, New York. Col-   *Av. 2948 ± 170*
lected, 1938. This is early Point Peninsula Focus (cf.
W. A. Ritchie, Rochester Museum of Arts and Sciences, *Memoir 1* [1944], pp. 152–60). Submitted by
W. A. Ritchie.

C-288   *Lamoka:* Charcoal from hearth in subsoil under 5 feet   4395 ± 350
of undisturbed refuse at Lamoka Lake site, Schuyler   4344 ± 300
County, New York. Some rootlets were present in   *Av. 4369 ± 200*

Our No.	Sample	Age (Years)

this sample. They were segregated under a low-power magnifying glass. This sample was less carefully collected than No. C-367. Collected by A. Frank Barratt. Submitted by W. A. Ritchie. Comment: Doubt that all rootlets were removed. In view of rootlets, perhaps the 5383 date for No. C-367 should be taken.

C-367   *Lamoka (Lamoka III)*: Charcoal from Lamoka Lake site, Schuyler County, New York. From earliest occupation level 5 feet below midden surface. Probably this sample was more suitable than No. 288. Submitted by W. A. Ritchie.

5383 ± 250

C-794   *Point Peninsula:* Charcoal from the Hunter site on Red Lake in Jefferson County, New York. This charcoal represents a residue of a crematory fire. Small bits of what appear to be burned leather shroud fragments are included. The particular grave yielding the samples submitted was one of several closely clustered on a sand ridge adjacent to a group of stone crematories. The cremated bones, charcoal, offerings, etc., had been scooped from the crematories and buried in graves ranging in depth from 30 to 74 inches. This sample occurred in burial No. 1 at depths from about 25 to 30 inches from the surface, in direct association with cremated bones and grave goods, and was covered by clean, moist, undisturbed sand. There is no doubt as to its source or provenience. The total assemblage in the light of diagnostic grave goods is Point Peninsula 2 Focus, or classic Point Peninsula in New York, Ontario, and elsewhere in the Northeast (see W. A. Ritchie, *Am. Antiquity*, 17, 130–36 [1951]). This material was collected and submitted by W. A. Ritchie.

4881 ± 400
3920 ± 300
Av. 4400 ± 260

C-943   *Sunken Forest in Eastchester, New York (Pelham Bay)*: At Throggs Neck, Eastchester, submerged tree stumps occur. There is a sea wall on one end behind a beach and a low rocky point terminating in a short pier on the other. A small patch of original Spartina salt-grass association some 30 feet long and 10 feet wide remains margined on one side by fill brought for a road and breaking off on the bayward side with a 2-foot bank of black peaty soil that is eroded by high tides during winter storms. At the foot of this perpendicular bank there are mussels and other maritime denizens. The sunken forest starts from about the mid-tide mark and extends out into 8 or 10 feet of water. The outermost stumps

2830 ± 220

Our No.	Sample	Age (Years)

are not exposed even in the lowest tides. This sample came from a stump with cross-section diameters at ground level of about 1.5 and 2.5 feet. It scarcely protruded above the surface at low tide, and its radiating roots had an over-all diameter of about 6 feet. It was about 6 feet below the level of the Spartina flat and about 4.5 feet below the high-tide mark. Submitted by William J. Robbins, New York Botanical Garden.

C. ILLINOIS, INDIANA, IOWA, KENTUCKY, MICHIGAN, OHIO, PENNSYLVANIA, AND KANSAS

C-116   *Annis Mound, Kentucky (Webb I)*: Annis Mound, Kentucky. Archaic period, shell from the 6.5-foot level. Shells powdery on surface but shiny and apparently untouched underneath. Submitted by W. S. Webb, University of Kentucky.
           5149 ± 300

C-180   *Annis Mound, Kentucky (Webb IV)*: Annis Mound shell from the 3.0-foot level. Submitted by W. S. Webb.
           7374 ± 500

C-251   *Annis Mound, Kentucky (Deer Antler)*: Annis Mound deer antler from Archaic 6.5-foot level. Submitted by W. S. Webb.
           4900 ± 250

C-254   *Indian Knoll, Kentucky (Indian Knoll)*: Antler from Indian Knoll Oh2 mound at 1.0-foot level. Submitted by W. S. Webb.
           $\begin{cases} 5709 \pm 350 \\ 4894 \pm 560 \end{cases}$
           Av. 5302 ± 300

C-126   *Adena, Kentucky (Adena I)*: Adena material from Drake Mound, Fayette County, Kentucky, Site 11. Fragments of bark preserved by contact with copper reel-shaped breastplate in association with Burial 7, lying on bottom of pit, the central feature of this site. Submitted by W. S. Webb.
           1168 ± 150

C-214   *Adena, Ohio (Ohio Adena)*: Adena material from Cowan Creek Mound, Ohio. Charcoal from subfloor fireplace just outside house structure. Submitted by R. S. Baby, Ohio State Museum.
           1509 ± 250

C-136   *Hopewell, Ohio (Hopewell III)*: Charcoal from Altar 1, Section 3, Mound 25. Hopewell Mound Group, Ross County, Ohio. Excavated in 1891. Specimen 56424, Chicago Natural History Museum. Submitted by G. Quimby, Chicago Natural History Museum.
           1951 ± 200

C-137   *Hopewell, Ohio (Hopewell Shell)*: Conch shells associated with Skeletons 260 and 261, Section 3, almost certainly from Mound 25, Hopewell Mound Group,
           2285 ± 210

Our No.	Sample	Age (Years)
	Ross County, Ohio. Specimens 56358 and 56606, Chicago Natural History Museum. Submitted by G. Quimby.	
C-139	*Hopewell, Ohio (Hopewell I)*: Bark associated with Skeleton 248, Section 2, Mound 25, Hopewell Mound Group, Ross County, Ohio. Specimen 56094, Chicago Natural History Museum. Submitted by G. Quimby.	2044 ± 250
C-152	*Hopewell, Illinois (Hopewell II)*: Wood from wood and bark capping, lower edge of primary mound, Mound 9, Havana Group, Havana, Illinois. Submitted by Thorne Deuel, Illinois State Museum.	2336 ± 250
C-465	*Oxford, Ohio (Goldthwait)*: Large log from the Tazewell or Cary drift near Oxford, Ohio; Hamilton, Ohio, Quadrangle, Oxford Township, Section 26, just north of the creek. Submitted by R. P. Goldthwait, Ohio State University.	At least 15,000
C-364	*Tolleston, Illinois (Tolleston)*: Wood from Tolleston level, Lake Chicago (may be Algonquin instead). Log found at base of lake sand overlying till in clay pit at Dalton, Illinois. Submitted by J Harlen Bretz, University of Chicago.	3469 ± 230
C-466	*Till, Illinois (Illinoian)*: Wood found in till directly below Illinoian gumbotil in Vermillion County, Illinois. Submitted by G. W. White, Department of Geology, University of Illinois.	Older than 17,000
C-535	*Wedron, Illinois (Tazewell)*: Early Tazewell Shelbyville wood from Lake Kickapoo, Wedron, La Salle County, Illinois. This is supposed to be our only truly authentic Tazewell sample. Submitted by C. L. Horberg and J Harlen Bretz. (Cf. No. C-575.)	13,842 ± 780
C-575	*Wedron, Illinois (Wedron)*: Wood from Lake Kickapoo deposits at Wedron, Illinois. From dark peaty silt occurring in a bedrock valley in St. Peter sandstone in the same quarry and position as No. C-535. The wood horizon is overlain by periglacially deformed sand and dark silt, which in turn underlie laminated clay (Lake Kickapoo deposits). These lie under a series of tills which have been regionally correlated by C. L. Horberg and others. The lowest of these is Bloomington, so the sediments must be early Tazewell (either Bloomington or Shelbyville). This sample was collected by J Harlen Bretz and transmitted by Jerry Olson, University of Chicago. It was taken as a check on No. C-535.	Older than 17,000

Our No.	Sample	Age (Years)
C-510	*Farm Creek, Illinois (Farmdale)*: Wood from Farm Creek, Illinois, representing the earliest stages of the Wisconsin glaciation. Found 3–4 feet below the surface of the Farmdale loess. Submitted by Guy D. Smith, Bureau of Plant Industry, Beltsville, Maryland.	Older than 20,000
C-481	*Skunk Creek, Iowa (Skunk Creek)*: Wood found beneath a presumably Mankato till on north bank of Skunk Creek, NE. ¼, Sec. 15, T. 80 N., R. 22 W., Polk County, Iowa. Submitted by W. H. Scholtes, Iowa State College, Ames, Iowa.	Older than 17,000
C-528	*Clear Creek, Iowa:* Glacial wood collected in glacial till in Story County, Iowa. Location south side of Clear Creek in an exposed cut; N.E. 1; SW. 1; Sec. 5, T. 83 N., R. 24 W. Till thought to be Mankato. The wood was excavated by digging and found in loess which underlies a recent till. Submitted by W. H. Scholtes.	16,367 ± 1000
C-438	*Bridgeville, Pennsylvania (Bridgeville)*: Peat found beneath 17 feet of alluvial deposit just west of Bridgeville, Pennsylvania. Thought to be Tazewell or Cary. Submitted by E. R. Eller, Carnegie Museum, Pittsburgh.	Older than 16,000
C-526	*Bellevue, Ohio (Lake Lundy)*: Wood from Bellevue, Ohio, ¾ mile northwest of Castalia on the 620 contour. This falls within the higher limit of Lake Lundy (Grassmere) but above the Elkston limit. Lake Warren beaches are 50–60 feet higher. Submitted by R. P. Goldthwait.	8513 ± 500
C-508	*Camden Moraine, Ohio (Camden)*: Wood from Camden moraine, south of Dayton, Ohio. No. C-465 was from the outer limit of the drift of which the Camden moraine is a recessional moraine. This may be Cary. Submitted by R. P. Goldthwait.	Older than 17,000
C-509	*Farmdale, Illinois (Farmdale II)*: Wood found 0 to 1 foot below surface of the Farmdale loess at Farm Creek, Illinois. Same site as No. C-510. Submitted by Guy D. Smith.	Older than 19,000
C-500	*Lake Cicott:* Peat from Lake Cicott bog, Indiana. Collected from 22- to 23-foot depth, combined Samples B, G, H, I, L, M. Thought to be Zone C-1, Zone B boundary. Collected by J. E. Potzger, Butler University, Indianapolis, Indiana. Submitted by E. S. Deevey, Jr.	5625 ± 310
C-596	*Skunk River, Iowa (Cary II)*: Glacial wood from quarry near Ames. Found in the center of NW. ¼, Sec.	10,369 ± 700 12,798 ± 660

Our No.	Sample	Age (Years)

24, T. 84 N., R. 24 W., Story County, on east side of *Av. 11,952 ± 500*
Skunk River about 90 feet above the valley bottom.
Desiccated swell and swale upland bordering the
Skunk River; maximum relief of 120 feet reached
about ½ mile southeast of the river, now modified by
quarrying operations (see U.S.G.S. Topogr. Quadr.,
Ames, Iowa [1914]). The stratigraphy is Mankato
till about 30 feet thick above the Mississippian limestone bedrock. The sample, which consisted of wood,
was found about 25 feet below the surface in the unoxidized zone, which was gray, dry, and very hard
and had to be blasted to remove the sample. The
layer consisted of fine clay, silt, and sand, most of it
with some pebbles present. The oxidized to unoxidized gradational boundary occurred about 12 feet
below the surface, which was covered with timber.
The sample was about 3 inches in diameter and 2 feet
long before blasting to remove. Collected by Ronald
E. Wilcox, Department of Geology, Iowa State College, Ames. Submitted by R. F. Flint, Yale University.

C-653 *Skunk River, Iowa (Ames):* Glacial wood from the   12,161 ± 540
same quarry as No. C-596. It consisted of about   12,286 ± 800
twelve pieces up to 6 inches in length and 1 or 2 inches   *Av. 12,200 ± 500*
in diameter. They all came originally from one piece
of wood situated in a small pocket of sand in the
same till as No. C-596. The sand pocket was about 3
feet above and 12 feet west of the position of the
other piece of wood. Submitted by C. S. Gwynne,
Iowa State College, Ames.

C-664 *Skunk River, Iowa (Ames Top Drift):* Wood from   14,042 ± 1000
the Ames quarry (cf. Nos. C-596 and C-653, which
dated 11,952 ± 500 and 12,200 ± 500). This wood, unlike the earlier samples, is not from the till but from
a zone about 1 foot thick of stratified sand and silt
lying between the upper and lower tills at a depth of
28 feet from the surface. The top of this stratified
zone contains occasional root fragments, seemingly
in place. This sample probably came from the stump
of a tree that grew where it was found. Collected by
Wayne Williams and Bob Tench. Submitted by C. S.
Gwynne.

C-674 *Lake Chicago Sands, Chicago (Tolleston):* Wood from   8200 ± 480
Lake Chicago sands on University of Chicago cam-
pus, corner of Fifty-eighth Street and Ellis Avenue,
surface elevation 592 feet. Found in horizontal posi-
sition overlain by stratified sand at depth of 14 feet,

according to workman who found it. The section at
this locality is sand stratified with some silt layers,
0–19 feet; blue clay (till)with some sand and gravel,
19–57 feet. Professors Bretz and Horberg, of the University of Chicago, are of the opinion that this sand
represents a Tolleston and post-Tolleston lake deposit and that at a depth of 14 feet the sand is probably
Tolleston. Low beach ridges superposed on the sand
at the location occupy the position of the Algoma
stage of the lake. Submitted by C. L. Horberg.

C-675   *Plum Creek, Dyer, Indiana (Calumet)*: Wood from   1850 ± 480
        alluvial fill along Plum Creek near Dyer (SW. $\frac{1}{4}$, SE.
        $\frac{1}{4}$, Sec. 32, T. 35 N., R. 15 E.). The specimen was
        found at a depth of about 10 feet in the alluvial fill
        and about 2 feet above the base, which was in con-
        tact with glacial fill. Fill represents the Calumet and
        post-Calumet deposit (Bretz, *Illinois Geol. Surv.
        Bull.*, **65**, 117 [1939])., and the wood from near the
        base of the fill is probably of Calumet age. Shells, a
        mammoth tooth, and numerous fragments of deer
        antlers are associated. The shells, identified by F. C.
        Baker, differ from those found in definitely dated
        Tolleston sediments. Collected by J Harlen Bretz
        and C. L. Horberg. Submitted by C. L. Horberg.

C-684   *Wilson Hopewell Site, White County, Illinois (Wilson*   710 ± 310
        Hopewell): Charcoal from a fire pit in the corner of   736 ± 200
        a log tomb in Mound Wh°6 in White County, Illinois   *Av. 723 ± 180*
        (Wilson site). This fire pit was in association with
        seven burials, grave goods of positive Hopewellian
        affiliation. There was evidence in the stratigraphic
        profiles that there was no intrusion into the tomb in
        recent times and that the charcoal is therefore of
        definite Hopewellian origin. There were deposits of
        reworked limestone throughout the fill of the
        mound, and the log-roofing rafters over the tomb
        were largely discernible because of this redeposited
        limestone. Collected by Melvin Fowler, Illinois State
        Museum, Springfield. Submitted by Fred Eggan,
        University of Chicago.

C-738   *Archaic Kentucky Indian Sites:* Submitted by W. S.
C-739   Webb. The descriptions are as follows:
C-740
C-741

        C-738   *Annis Shell Mound, Butler County (Ken-*   4289 ± 300
                tucky Archaic I): Deer antler from the 1.5-,
                2.0-, and 2.5-foot levels at Site Bt 5, the

Our No.	Sample	Age (Years)

Annis shell mound. This sample was taken entirely from a band 1.5 feet thick, the top of which was within 1 foot of the mound surface. It is to be correlated with Nos. C-116, C-180, and C-251 from the same mound, which gave 5149 ± 300, 7374 ± 500, and 4900 ± 250, respectively. However, Nos. C-116 and C-180 consisted of rather powdery shell, which was somewhat dubious; No. C-251 was deer antler from the 6.5-foot level.

C-739   *Annis Shell Mound, Butler County (Kentucky Archaic II)*: Deer antler from the 5.5-, 6.0-, 6.5-, and 7.0-foot levels. This sample came from a band 2 feet thick at the bottom of the mound. Again this sample should correlate with Nos. C-116, C-180, and C-251, as well as with No. C-738. No. C-251 was from the same level. 4333 ± 450

C-740   *Indian Knoll Shell Mound, Ohio County (Kentucky Archaic III)*: Deer antler from a band 6 inches thick at the 1-foot level. This material is similar to No. C-254, which gave 5302 ± 300. 4282 ± 250

C-741   *Indian Knoll Shell Mound, Ohio County (Kentucky Archaic IV)*: Deer antler from the 4.5-foot level, from a band 6 inches thick near the bottom of the mound. The total depth of of the mound is 7 feet. This is the same site as Nos. C-254 and C-740. 3963 ± 350

C-759   *Kentucky Adena I:* Charcoal from an Adena mound at Dover, Mason County, Kentucky, Site Ms 27. The charcoal came from a large heavily burned area near the top of the mound core. It bears the donor's sample No. 117 (V 42). Collected and submitted by W. S. Webb. 2650 ± 170

C-760   *Kentucky Adena II:* Charcoal associated with Burial No. 55 in the Adena mound at Dover, Mason County, Kentucky, Site Ms 27. Burial 55 was a redeposited cremation near the mound base outside the skirt of the mound core and was entirely covered by a heavy earth mantle. This sample bears the collector's sample No. 148 (V 38). Collected and submitted by W. S. Webb. 2260 ± 220
 2078 ± 290
 Av. 2169 ± 175

C-801   *Glenwood:* Wood from beach deposits apparently of the Glenwood stage of glacial Lake Chicago, found 1 mile west of Dyer, Indiana, NE. $\frac{1}{4}$, Sec. 30, T. 35 $10,661 \pm 460$
 $11,284 \pm 600$
 Av. 10,972 ± 350

Our No.	Sample	Age (Years)

N., R. 15 E., Illinois. The specimens were found at a depth of 8 feet in a deposit of beach ridge sand and gravel containing associated lagoonal deposits. The thickness of the deposit ranges from 6 to 18 feet and has a composition dominantly of inclined beds of sand and gravel with thin interbedded layers of silt and fine sand. Following Bretz, the deposits of the Glenwood stage are considered to be late Cary age. Collected and submitted by C. L. Horberg.

C-846   *Dune Buried Peat, South Haven, Michigan (South Haven II)*: The peat layer described in No. C-848 was sampled at the bottom portion. Submitted by J. H. Zumberge, University of Michigan, J Harlen Bretz, and C. L. Horberg.   6744 ± 530

C-848   *Dune Buried Log, South Haven, Michigan (South Haven I)*: A white pine log taken from a layer of peat on the eastern shore of Lake Michigan at South Haven. The layer is covered by sand dunes. There was a 30-inch layer in which the bits of wood, the pine log constituting this sample, were buried. Collected and submitted by J. H. Zumberge, J Harlen Bretz, and C. L. Horberg.   { 6232 310 / 6659 ± 350 / *Av. 6440 ± 230*

C-849   *Dune Buried Peat, South Haven, Michigan (South Haven III)*: Peat from the uppermost portion of the peat layer described in No. C-848. Submitted by J. H. Zumberge, J Harlen Bretz, and C. L. Horberg.   4816 ± 290

C-871   *Glenwood (Glenwood II)*: Wood from woody layer at the bottom of a sand and gravel deposit at Dyer, Indiana, NE. ½, Sec. 30, T. 35 N., R. 15 E., Illinois. Taken at a depth of 12 feet below the top of the sand spit from the northernmost of the sand pits now opened. Same deposit as that from which No. C-801 was obtained. Collected September 15, 1953, and submitted by J Harlen Bretz.   18,500 ± 500

C-872   *Dyer, Indiana, Deposit (Glenwood III)*: Peat from lagoon deposit buried beneath the Dyer spit where No. C-871 was obtained. Original depth of burial was about 15 feet. Collected and submitted September 15, 1953, by J Harlen Bretz.   Older than 21,000

C-874   *Florence Mound (Florence Mound)*: Charcoal from an Adena mound known as the Florence Mound in Pickaway County, near Fox, Ohio. This consisted of charcoal from a ceremonial fireplace on the floor of the mound. Collected and submitted by R. S. Baby.   1425 ± 250

C-893   *Tazewell (Tazewell)*: Log collected near Central Ohio in Licking County, 4.5 miles southwest of Newark,   16,100 ± 850

at a point 300 feet south of Ramp Creek and 500 feet
east of the New York Central Railroad. This piece
occurred 49 feet below the surface in an excavation
for a hydraulic press of the Kaiser Aluminum Plant
in 1952. At the surface are 5–15 feet of alluvial sand
and gravel; below this is somewhat more than 60 feet
of homogenous dark-gray till. Twigs and a few logs
were recovered from a depth of 45–60 feet.

This till fills the mid-Pleistocene (Yarmouth?)
buried Newark Valley known from wells 200–300
feet to bedrock. It is 5 miles west of the distinct outer
limit of silty Wisconsin drift. On the other hand, it
lies 5 miles east of (outside) a clay-rich drift believed
to be Cary (Johnstown moraine). All indications are
that the logs were swept up and deposited by the
Tazewell advance and that the surface was covered
with thin outwash from the Johnstown moraine in
Cary time. Excavated and submitted by R. P. Gold-
thwait.

C-899   *Barbeau Creek Rock Shelter (Barbeau Creek I–IX):*
C-900   The ancient Indian site located at Modoc near
C-903   Prairie du Rocher, Illinois, was investigated by a
C-904   new field methodology. The site itself has consider-
C-904'   able intrinsic interest. It consists of a 25.5-foot-deep
C-905   midden deposit and is situated at the base of an 82-
C-907   foot sandstone bluff that projects over and protects
C-908   the site. It obviously belongs to the Archaic period,
and from an analysis of the artifacts it is clear
that a great deal can be learned from this site about
cultural change and development during the Archaic
period. In addition, information about its age will be
useful in establishing geologic and climatologic
conditions in the area. The samples to be measured
were processed in the field by Frederick R. Matson,
of State College, Pennsylvania. The method used by
Matson was new and was designed to facilitate collection of samples for dating from other sites. Four
procedures were used:

1. *A hand-picked specimen, using a spatula and
shielding the palm of the hand with aluminum foil.*—
This concentration of material from charcoal-rich
soil is contaminated only with a thin coating of
soil and possibly with rootlets that are prevalent
throughout the site. There are calcareous deposits
throughout the site to a slight extent.

2. *Material washed in water.*—The charcoal that
floated on top of the bucket of water was collected on

a well-washed copper-wire screen (approximately 114 mesh) from a hardware store. After the sample was dried, the charcoal was placed on a piece of aluminum foil, and fragments of rock and as many rootlets as possible were removed.

3. *Material that passed through the copper screen mentioned above but was retained on a 20-mesh and a 115-mesh sieve.*—This material was submitted only because of its general interest; it is contaminated with rootlets and rock fragments and may not be of prime interest for measurement. The samples were saved, however, because at some sites the charcoal fragments may be no larger than these. It would be very tedious to separate all the rock from the charcoal, but slight agitation in water effectively increases the charcoal content of the sample.

4. *Samples collected in the field and untouched in the field laboratory.*—These jars have not been opened since they were taken from the excavation. They were submitted only to round out the possible series. It was not suggested that they be tested. They are charcoal-rich soils and are similar to the material from which the samples obtained by procedure No. 1 were concentrated.

The site itself was divided into three stratigraphic zones.

Series A: 178–186 inches in depth.—The charcoal occurs in brown sandy soil within a few inches above ash beds and red burned clay areas that may have been hearths. This zone is particularly rich in flints and flint chips. A copper awl and a fragment of a ground and polished bannerstone were found. This is an important and fairly broad occupation zone.

Series B: 250–262 inches in depth.—This broad zone of charcoal-flecked soil is again just above ash levels and red-clay hearth areas. Several pits and a few postholes reached from this level into the next lower one, which is a charcoal-free band of yellow sandy soil about 2 feet thick; it is practically free of cultural material and was built up in a series of bands which suggest varves. The zone just above this yellow soil from which the charcoal was collected was quite rich in cultural material. Apparently this marks the reoccupation of the site after a considerable period of sandy soil deposition (by water?).

Series C: 280–307 inches in depth.—This is the lowest occupation level found at the site. Test drilling at lower levels yielded no cultural debris. It is of course

Our No.	Sample	Age (Years)

possible that further excavation of more extended areas would uncover occupation levels at greater depths, but at present there is no indication of this. Relatively few flint implements, but many flint chips, some worked, occur in this zone.

The samples were furnished by H. D. Winters, of the University of Chicago, and Frederick R. Matson. The notations in parentheses after each sample number indicate the zone from which and the procedure by which the sample was taken. For example, the notation A–2 means that the sample was taken from Zone A by procedure 2.

C-899	(A–1)	5955 ± 235
C-900	(A–2)	5268 ± 230
C-903	(B–1)	8546 ± 380
C-904	(B–2)	$10,947 \pm 900$
C-904'	(B–2)	7800 ± 900
C-905	(B–3)	$11,200 \pm 800$
C-907	(C–1)	$10,651 \pm 650$
C-908	(C–2)	9101 ± 440

C-912   *Lizard Creek* (*Lizard Creek I*): Wood presumably either of early Mankato or early Cary age from a deposit in Webster County, Iowa, 2.5 miles northwest of Ford Dodge (SE. corner, SW. $\frac{1}{4}$, Sec. 10, T. 89 N., R. 29 W.). The stratigraphy is (i) 10 feet 4 inches calcareous Mankato outwash; (ii) 7 feet 4 inches calcareous Mankato till; (iii) 10 feet 0 inches calcareous outwash (early Mankato? or Cary?): wood from *oxidized calcareous bedded sand* 6.5 feet below top of this outwash horizon, same stratigraphic level as No. C-913; (iv) 3 feet 7 inches calcareous till (early Mankato? or Cary?): exposed. Submitted by W. H. Scholtes and R. V. Ruhe, U S. Department of Agriculture Soil Conservation Service, Iowa State College.
         $12,120 \pm 530$

C-913   *Lizard Creek* (*Lizard Creek II*): Wood from the same site as No. C-912 except it came from *unoxidized* portion of the glacial drift bed. The stratigraphy is (i) 10 feet 4 inches calcareous Mankato outwash; (ii) 7 feet 4 inches calcareous Mankato till; (iii) 10 feet 0 inches calcareous outwash (early Mankato? or Cary?): wood from *unoxidized calcareous bedded silt* 5 feet 10 inches to 7 feet 0 inches below top of this outwash horizon, same stratigraphic level as No. C-912; (iv) 3 feet 7 inches calcareous till (early Mankato? or Cary?): exposed. Submitted by W. H Scholtes and R. V. Ruhe.
         $13,300 \pm 900$

Our No.	Sample	Age (Years)
C-923	*Toepfner Mound (Toepfner Mound I)*: Charred logs from a tomb in a large Adena mound in Columbus, Ohio, known as the Toepfner Mound. These logs occurred 7.5 feet above the floor of the mound. The sample was labeled "Feature II." Submitted by R. S. Baby.	2377 ± 150
C-942	*Toepfner Mound (Toepfner Mound II)*: Charcoal samples from the Toepfner Mound described in No. C-923. This material came from 4.4 feet above the floor of the mound. It was labeled "Feature VII." Submitted by R. S. Baby.	2780 ± 410
C-928	*Kansas Woodland (Kansas Woodland)*: Wood charcoal collected from the Missouri Basin in the course of the River Basin Survey's archeological excavation at the site near Woodruff, Phillips County, Kansas. This site is representative of the sites of one of the early pottery-making groups that has been estimated to have occupied the area somewhere between 1000 and 2000 years ago. No remains belonging to that general period west of the Missouri River have been dated.	1343 ± 240

The charcoal was found in a burial site attributed to the Keith focus of the Woodland pattern. The site has been reported by M. F. Kivett in a paper entitled "The Woodruff Ossuary: A Prehistoric Burial Site in Phillips County, Kansas" (*U.S. Bur. Am. Ethnol. Bull. 154*, "River Basin Surveys," Paper No. 3 [1953]). In Kivett's opinion, "the Keith focus probably represents one of the earliest Woodland variants in this area," perhaps preceding in time the Hopewellian culture of the lower Missouri-Illinois valleys. The Woodland materials of the Central Plains are not yet very well known. They evidently include the earliest pottery yet found in the region, and in part, at least, they may be prehorticultural. Unlike some of the later archeological horizons of the region, none none of the Woodland complexes so far investigated has yielded any cross-finds of southwestern pottery or other fairly good time indicators. In short, any chronological leads to be obtained from the present charcoal sample will probably throw much-needed light on a prehistoric period for which we have no good leads. Submitted by Frank H. H. Roberts, Jr., and Waldo R. Wedel, Smithsonian Institution.

C-935	*Glacial Wood from Poag, Madison County, Illinois (Edwardsville Well Wood)*: Wood from 70-foot depth in Edwardsville city water well at Poag. Location:	Older than 21,600

Our No.	Sample	Age (Years)

NE. ¼ NE. ¼ SE. ¼, Sec. 13, T. 4 N., R. 9 W. This well is located on a terrace that is probably late Mankato in age. Submitted by M. M. Leighton, Illinois Geological Survey.

C-937   *Glacial Wood from Hartford, Illinois (Hartford Well Wood)*: Glacial wood thought to belong to the Mankato or to an older Ice Age found in a well at a depth of 100–110 feet, at Hartford, Madison County. Location: NE. ¼ NE. ¼ SW. ¼, Sec. 33, T. 5 N., R. 9 W. The well, known as the Ranney Collector Well, was dug at the Shell Oil Company loading dock at Hartford. Submitted by M. M. Leighton.   Older than 24,000

D. Alabama, North Carolina, South Carolina, and West Virginia

C-336   *West Virginia Boreal:* Peat of Pollen Zone B (pine) from 12 feet 3 inches to 12 feet 9 inches in Cranberry Glades, West Virginia. Submitted by H. C. Darlington, Marshall College.   9434 ± 840

C-474   *Singletary Lake, North Carolina (Singletary Optimum)*: Peat from highest of the three organic horizons at Singletary Lake, North Carolina. Same site as No. C-475. Submitted by David G. Frey, University of North Carolina.   10,224 ± 510

C-475   *Singletary Lake, North Carolina (Singletary Mankato)*: Peat and lake sediments from Singletary Lake, North Carolina. The lake has three organic horizons. This sample is the second which has been tentatively identified from pollen as lying between the Mankato and Cary substages. Submitted by David G. Frey.   Older than 20,000

C-476   *Singletary Lake, North Carolina (Singletary Cary)*: Lowest of three layers in Singletary Lake (cf. No. C-475). Submitted by David G. Frey.   Older than 20,000

C-363   *Santee, South Carolina (Santee)*: Cyprus wood from a large stump buried under 30 feet of sand deposited by the Santee River in South Carolina. Stump was 11 feet in diameter, larger than any now growing in the region. Submitted by Stephen Taber, University of South Carolina.   Older than 17,000

C-105   *Myrtle Beach, South Carolina (Myrtle Beach)*: Cyprus wood from the Myrtle Beach area under the Pamlico Terrace. Submitted by Stephen Taber.   Older than 20,000

C-755 C-756   *Perry Site Shell Mound, Lu°25, Tennessee River, Alabama (Alabama Archaic)*: Deer antler from the 4-foot level (No. C-755) and the 3.5-foot level (No.   4764 ± 250

C-756), mixed about equally to afford sufficient carbon for measurement. The Perry Site, Lu°25, Unit 1 (see *U.S. Bur. Am. Ethnol. Bull. 129* [1942], by W. S. Webb and D. L. DeJarnette) was an ancient shell mound about 500 yards from the upper end of Seven Mile Island, which lies between the Wilson and Pickwick dams on the Tennessee River in Alabama. It was 200 by 300 feet and about 10 feet thick at its thickest point. The archeological stratigraphy indicates that the Alabama shell mounds began earlier than those in Kentucky (Annis and Indian Knoll; Nos. C-116, C-180, C-251, C-254, C-738, C-739, C-740, C-741). These samples, together with those from the Archaic Kentucky mounds, indicate when Archaic man ceased to build shell mounds in the southeastern United States. Presumably this occurred when he had developed an economy independent of shellfish as a staple food supply. Submitted by W. S. Webb.

E. LOUISIANA, MISSISSIPPI, MISSOURI, NEBRASKA, GEORGIA, AND TEXAS

C-143　*Crooks Site, Louisiana (Quimby IV)*: Charcoal from secondary mantle near junction with primary mantle of east slope Mound A, Crooks Site, La–3, La Salle Parish, Marksville period in Louisiana. Submitted by G. Quimby.　　　　　　　　1158 ± 250

C-150　*Tchefuncte, Louisiana (Quimby II)*: Charcoal from top 6 inches, Tchefuncte Site ST 2, Midden A, in Louisiana. Submitted by G. Quimby.　　　　　633 ± 150

C-151　*Tchefuncte, Louisiana (Quimby III)*: Shell from top 6 inches of same Tchefuncte site as No. C-150. Submitted by G. Quimby.　　　　　　　　1233 ± 250

C-154　*Bynum Site, Mississippi (Bynum II)*: Bynum vegetal material from Site MCs–16, in Mississippi, base Mound B. Submitted by John Cotter, National Park Service.　　　　　　　　1276 ± 150

C-385　*Bonfils, Missouri (Bonfils I)*: Wood from the Bonfils sand terrace near the mouth of the Missouri River. This terrace is a remnant of the Festus Terrace, and the date therefore should apply to the Festus Terrace. Sample taken from 2 feet above top of the gravel. Submitted by Louis C. Peltier, Washington University at St. Louis.　　　　　12,148 ± 700

C-65　*Medicine Creek, Nebraska (Schultz I)*: Charcoal from Medicine Creek Site Ft–50 in Nebraska. It is a mix-　　　5256 ± 350

Our No.	Sample	Age (Years)
	ture of soil bands A and B, which are 2 feet apart. Submitted by C. B. Schultz, University of Nebraska.	
C-108a	*Medicine Creek, Nebraska (Schultz III)*: Charcoal from Soil B at Ft–50 in Nebraska. Submitted by C. B. Schultz.	8274 ± 500
C-470	*Medicine Creek, Nebraska (Schultz II)*: Charcoal from Soil B at Ft–50, lower occupation Zone Feature 18, N. 155/E. 45. Collected later and more carefully, otherwise duplicate of No. C-108a. Submitted by C. B. Schultz.	$10,493 \pm 1500$
C-471	*Lime Creek:* Lime Creek site charcoal, Ft–41, Frontier County, Nebraska. Reference: *Lime Creek Bulletin*, page 34 (cf. Schultz, 1948, p. 34). Submitted by C. B. Schultz.	$\begin{cases} 9880 \pm 670 \\ 9167 \pm 600 \end{cases}$ *Av. 9524 ± 450*
C-558	*Folsom Bone:* Burned bison bone from Lubbock, Texas, from the Folsom horizon. Submitted by E. H. Sellards, Texas Memorial Museum, Austin, Texas. Mr. Sellards' description: "This burned bone has been collected by Glen Evans and Grayson Meade of our staff. We are entirely satisfied that the horizon is Folsom. This conclusion that it is Folsom is based on two principal observations. We have, as you know, a thoroughly proven section at Clovis, New Mexico, the succession being a gray sand containing elephant, other fossils, and artifacts as the basal stratum of the section, followed by a deposit containing a large percentage of diatomaceous earth as the second stratum. The elephant is absent from this second stratum and instead we have an abundance of bison. At the Lubbock locality exactly these conditions are repeated, gray sand as the basal stratum with elephant as the most common fossil, followed by the diatomaceous material with the extinct bison as the abundant fossil. Later units are present at both localities. At the Clovis locality the Folsom culture is contained in and confined to this second horizon. At the Lubbock locality Folsom culture is present as shown by the fact that we have found Folsom points thrown out in the course of dredging. We have not yet found them in place in the diatomaceous deposit, but are fully convinced that they will be found in place as excavating proceeds."	9883 ± 350
C-377	*Secondary Channel, Folsom Site, New Mexico ("Folsom")*: Charcoal from a hearth in fill of secondary channel which had cut through the original deposit of bison bone and artifacts at the original Folsom site.	4575 ± 300 3923 ± 400 *Av. 4283 ± 250*

Our No.	Sample	Age (Years)

Collected July, 1933. Submitted by H. J. Cook, Agate, Nebraska.

C-469   *Cedar Canyon:* Charcoal from Cedar Canyon, Nebraska, locality Sx–101. Found in buried hearth as scribed in Figure 8, *Am. Naturalist*, **70**, 359. Submitted by C. B. Schultz.
         1993 ± 190
         2379 ± 430
     Av. 2147 ± 150

C-153   *Davis:* Corncobs from Davis site, in eastern Texas. No. 5888, Jones 3497. Submitted by Alex Krieger, University of Texas, through James Griffin, University of Michigan.
         1553 ± 175

C-645   *Soil, Red Cloud, Nebraska:* Buried soils from Schultz's
C-647   Terraces Nos. 1 and 2, south of Red Cloud. Terrace
C-649   1 is thought to be 2000–3000 years old, although several buried soils of rather weak profile development exist here, and there could be a fairly wide range of age. The soil actually taken on Terrace 1 was the lower part of a sort of double profile with a very thin horizon of light-colored material separating the layers. The Terrace 2 material should correlate very closely to the charcoal date (i.e., 9000–10,000 years). A serious effort was made at all points to exclude rootlets from the sample. Samples collected in 1949 by E. C. Reed, C. B. Schultz, H. Waite, and James Thorp. The organic matter in the soils analyzed: No. C-645, 0.66 per cent carbon; No. C-647, 0.45 per cent carbon; No. C-649, 0.47 per cent carbon. J. W. Borland, of the Beltsville Laboratories, Division of Soil Survey, U.S. Department of Agriculture, extracted these small amounts of carbon from the soil samples, preparing barium carbonate, which was submitted for analysis by James Thorp, Department of Botany, Earlham College, Richmond, Indiana.

C-645   *Soil Terrace II:* Soil sample from Terrace 2. Taken from a level about 30 feet below the top of Terrace 2. Buried by loess, it came from a dark grayish-brown and rust-mottled buried soil about 18–24 inches thick. It lay about 100 yards from No. C-647.
         7809 ± 400

C-647   *Nebraska Soil:* Soil sample from Terrace 2. Taken from a level about 30 feet below the top of Terrace 2 from a dark grayish-brown and rust-mottled buried soil about 18–24 inches thick. It lay about 100 yards from sample No. C-645.
         7426 ± 600

Our No.	Sample	Age (Years)

C-649   *Soil Terrace I:* Soil sample from Terrace 1.   4150 ± 350
Following is a cross-section from the surface
down: 0–18 inches, dark grayish-brown,
crumb-structured, calcareous silt loam; 18–
24 inches, calcareous loess; 24–36 inches,
black, granular, calcareous silt loam (a buried
soil); 36–48 inches, pale-brown, calcareous
loess with white line threads; 48–84 inches,
pale-brown calcareous laminated silt and
silty clay loam; 84–92 inches, light grayish-
brown, calcareous silt loam with prismatic
structure (a weakly developed buried soil
representing a short period of slow accumulation); 92–110 inches, black granular calcareous silty clay loam (black when wet; a
buried soil); 110–120 inches, light grayish-
brown calcareous silt loam, either loess or
alluvial silt; 120–134 inches, dark-gray
granular calcareous silty clay loam (this is
the A horizon of the buried soil that was
sampled [No. C-649]; the buried soils above
this level have many modern grass and tree
roots); 134–156 inches, prismatic calcareous
heavy silt loam; 156–216 inches, coarse
prismatic calcareous loesslike silt loam. The
plain of Louisa Creek lies 27 feet below the
top of Terrace 1 at this point.

C-698   *Kincaid Shelter, Edwards Plateau, Texas (Kincaid):*   1212 ± 300
Charcoal from the Kincaid Cave, Edwards Plateau,
Texas. The cave yielded a remarkably complete sequence of archeological and faunal stages, ranging
from early-man levels at the bottom to late prehistoric Indian horizons at the top. This sample is from
near the top, the deeper samples having had too little
charcoal to measure. This sample is from 20 feet
below the surface in a fire pit, Bed No. 6, dark-gray
zone of burned rock; Square G–H: B–9 (Square No. 4
near). Collected in 1951. Donor's sample No. 4. Submitted by Glen L. Evans, Texas Memorial Museum,
Austin.

C-822   *Cedar Canyon:* Charcoal from "soil" and hearth at   2049 ± 180
the base of Terrace 1 fill from site Sx–107, Cedar
Canyon area, Sioux County, Nebraska. This charcoal was collected in 1951 by Lloyd Tanner, Gilbert
C. Lueninghoener, and C. B. Schultz. It should furnish a date for the basal part of the Terrace 1 fill.

Our No.	Sample	Age (Years)

The earlier No. C-469 from the same locality, which dated 2379 ± 430 and 1993 ± 190, was from the middle of the Terrace 1 fill. The exact location from which the charcoal was taken was near the center of Sec. 16, T. 33 N., R. 53 W. (see Fig. 26, p. 186, and Pl. XV, p. 192, of "Pleistocene and Postglacial Mammals of Nebraska," by E. H. Barbour and C. B. Schultz, in *Early Man* [Philadelphia: Lippincott, 1937]). Submitted by C. B. Schultz.

C-824   *Medicine Creek Reservoir; Red Smoke Site (Red Smoke Site)*: Charcoal from the Red Smoke Site (Ft–42) in the Medicine Creek Reservoir Area, Frontier County, Nebraska. The charcoal was from a hearth in the middle portion of the Terrace 2A fill, located in Sec. 15, T. 5 N., R. 26 W. (see Schultz, Lueninghoener, and Frankforter, "A Graphic Résumé of the Pleistocene of Nebraska," *Bull. Univ. Nebraska State Museum*, **3**, No. 6 [1951], and David, *Am. Antiquity*, **18**, No. 4 [1953]). This sample was collected in 1950 by E. Mott Davis and associates. It bears the field number "UNSM 859-50." It would give a date which would be near to what is probably the climax of the Mankato. All the samples from Terrace 2A which previously have been run are from lower levels. Submitted by C. B. Schultz.

        8570 ± 300
        9153 ± 600
  Av. 8862 ± 230

C-930   *Cedar Canyon Charcoal (Cedar Canyon II)*: Charcoal from Sx–101, Cedar Canyon, Sioux County, Nebraska. In hearth associated with paleosol at base of Terrace 1 fill (15 feet below top of fill) in bottom of trench dug by University of Nebraska State Museum field party in 1936. This sample (collected in 1951 by Lloyd Tanner, Gilbert C. Lueninghoener, C. B. Schultz, and associates) gives an additional check on the date of the basal part of Terrace 1 fill. The charcoal is from a paleosol below the place where No. C-469, which dated 2147 ± 150 years, was taken in the same terrace fill and exposure. Submitted by C. B. Schultz.

    2675 ± 280

C-931   *Cedar Canyon Charcoal (Cedar Canyon III)*: Charcoal from Sx-101, Cedar Canyon, Sioux County, Nebraska. Sample associated with paleosol near top of Terrace 1 fill (25 inches below top of fill). This sample (collected in 1951 by Lloyd Tanner, Gilbert C. Lueninghoener, C. B. Schultz, and associates) is from a paleosol above the place where No. C-469 was

    3100 ± 410

Our No.	Sample	Age (Years)

taken in the same terrace fill and exposure. Submitted by C. B. Schultz.

C-933 *Booger Bottom Site (Booger Bottom)*: A site which is   2104 ± 140
an erosional remnant of an old natural levee in Georgia. Indians had lived on the site, located in the Buford Reservoir, between floods, throughout its life. Cultural material is quite homogenous from bottom to top. It represents a horizon found throughout the Southeast. It shows some connections with the Adena culture of Ohio and Kentucky. No dates are available as yet on this horizon.

Donor sample No. 53-131. Charcoal, Field Specimen No. 121. Site 9HL64 (Booger Bottom), Hall County, Georgia. Collected October 30, 1953. From post molds, Feature 16, Section 0–110, surface depth 8.2–8.7 feet in old natural levee. Associated with Cartersville Check Stamped pottery. Postholes originated in top of lowest occupation level. Material should date pure Cartersville Check Stamped horizon (Forsythe Period), and Wright Check Stamped horizon, which is present in some Adena mounds. Submitted by Charles H. Fairbanks, Ocmulgee National Monument.

F. Arizona, California, Colorado, and New Mexico

C-165 *Bat Cave:* Corncobs and wood fragments from the de-
C-173 bris in Bat Cave, New Mexico. The depth below the
C-172 top correlates with the development of corn from a
C-164 primitive form at the lowest layer of 6 feet to essen-
C-171 tially modern corn at the top. Excavated by Herbert
C-170 Dick. Submitted by P. C. Mangelsdorf, Harvard University.

Sample	Layer (Depth in Feet)	
C-165 (cobs)	0–1	1752 ± 250
C-173 (wood)	1–2	1907 ± 250
C-172 (wood)	2–3	2239 ± 250
C-164 and C-171 (corn and wood)	3–4	2249 ± 250
C-170 (wood)	4–5	2862 ± 250

C-567 *Bat Cave:* Charcoal all from one area in Bat Cave.
C-569 From levels from which there has been no vandalism
C-570 and little opportunity for mixture by rodent activity.
C-571 The development of the corn culture is presumably

Our No.	Sample	Age (Years)

C-572   correlatable with the charcoal dates. Submitted by
C-573   Paul C. Mangelsdorf.

Sample	Location	
C-567	Area III, Section I*c*, Front, 11–15 inches depth	1610 ± 200
C-569	Area III, Section I*c*, Rear, 24–36 inches depth	2816 ± 200
C-570	Area III, Section I*c*, Front, 36–48 inches depth	2048 ± 170
C-571	Area III, Section I*c*, Front, 48–60 inches depth	5605 ± 290
C-572	Area III, Section I*c*, Front, 54–66 inches depth	5000–7500 (poor run)
C-573	Area III, Section I*c*, Front, 60–66 inches depth	5931 ± 310

C-584   *Tularosa Cave I:* Corncobs from Tularosa Cave,   2223 ± 200
New Mexico. This sample of cobs was from Square
2R2, Level 14, the lowest preceramic occupation level
resting on sandstone bedrock 9 feet 4 inches from the
surface of the dry midden. Submitted by Paul S.
Martin, Chicago Natural History Museum.

C-585   *Tularosa Cave II:* Cobs and tree back from Tularosa $\begin{cases} 2112 \pm 230 \\ 2177 \pm 225 \end{cases}$
Cave, New Mexico. This sample was taken from   *Av. 2145 ± 160*
Square 2R2, Level 10, 6 feet 8 inches below the sur-
face. This layer is the Pine Lawn phase, the first pot-
tery-making period of the area. Submitted by Paul S.
Martin through Donald Collier, Chicago Natural
History Museum.

C-612   *Tularosa Cave III:* Corn and vegetable material from   2300 ± 200
Tularosa Cave (cf. Nos. C-584 and C-585), Square
2R2, Level 13. Pre-pottery and associated with
Chiricahua-type implements. Submitted by Paul S.
Martin.

C-186   *San Francisco Bay Mound, California (California Ar-* $\begin{cases} 633 \pm 200 \\ 911 \pm 180 \end{cases}$
chaic): Charcoal from a San Francisco Bay shell   *Av. 720 ± 130*
mound, Site 4–Mrn–115. Submitted by R. F. Heizer,
University of California, Berkeley.

C-440   *California Early Horizon:* Charcoal from near Sacra-   4052 ± 160
C-522   mento, Site SJo–68, culture early Central California
Horizon as described in Robert F. Heizer, *The
Archaeology of Central California. I. Early Horizon*
("Anthropological Records," **12**, No. 1 [University
of California Press, 1949]).

C-216   *Cochise, Arizona (Cochise)*: Charcoal-bearing dirt from   7756 ± 370
b^1 and b^2 beds shown in Figure 13, page 47, *The*

Our No.	Sample	Age (Years)

Cochise Culture ("Medallion Papers," No. XXIX). This is the Sulphur Springs stage of the culture. Submitted by E. B. Sayles, Arizona State Museum, Tucson.

C-511 *Cochise, Arizona (Sulphur Springs):* Charcoal from Cochise Site 6 North, Sulphur Springs stage. Submitted by E. B. Sayles. — 6210 ± 450

C-515 *Cochise, Arizona (Chiricahua):* Charcoal from Cochise Site 12, Chiricahua Stage. Submitted by E. B. Sayles. — 4006 ± 270

C-518 *Cochise, Arizona (San Pedro II):* Charcoal from Site 3, San Pedro stage. Sulphur Springs Valley, Arizona (cf. Pearce 8:9, Fig. 4). Submitted by E. B. Sayles. — 1762 ± 420

C-556 *Wet Leggett, New Mexico (Antevs I):* Cochise charcoal collected by Ernst Antevs on the Wet Leggett, New Mexico, August 17, 1950. Found in wall of an arroyo tributary to main Wet Leggett arroyo at a depth 9 feet 8 inches below the ground level in beds which may be either Chiricahua or San Pedro. Submitted by Ernst Antevs through G. Quimby. — 4508 ± 680

C-519 *Cochise, Arizona (San Pedro):* Charcoal from Cochise Site, San Pedro stage (Benson 5:10), Figure 8, Bed *b*. Submitted by E. B. Sayles. — 2463 ± 310

C-615 *Searles Lake:* Searles Lake, California, organic matter from mud seam separating upper and lower salt deposits of Searles Lake, believed to have been deposited by flood waters during last glaciation. Organic matter was extracted with acetone, evaporated to a thick syrup and the resinous material precipitated by adding water. Donor's sample No. 2. Submitted by W. A. Gale, American Potash and Chemical Corporation, Trona, California. — At least 16,000

C-628 *Big Sur:* Charcoal from shell midden on California coast at mouth of Willow Creek about 30 miles south of Big Sur on coast of Monterey County. Midden overlain by 10 feet of gravels. Present beach gravels submerge 4.5 feet of midden, indicating shore subsidence. Submitted by R. F. Heizer. — 1879 ± 250

C-451 *Lindenmeier Site, Colorado (Lindenmeier):* Charcoal obtained from a hearth in the fill of a secondary channel. Geologic evidence indicated that the age of of the hearth should be approximately half that of the occupational level from which the Folsom material was taken. Submitted by Frank H. H. Roberts. — 5020 ± 300

C-616 *Searles Lake:* No. C-615 consisted of organic matter from a mud seam separating the upper and lower salt — Older than 19,000

Our No.	Sample	Age (Years)
	deposits of Searles Lake, California. It is believed that the layer of organic matter was deposited by flood waters during the recession of the glaciers. The organic matter was extracted with acetone and evaporated to a thick syrup, and the resinous material precipitated by adding distilled water. No. C-615 dated at least 16,000 years old. The present sample was prepared in the same way, but from mud just below the lower deposit of soluble salts and therefore, of course, should be considerably older than No. C-615. Collected and submitted by W. A. Gale.	
C-617	*Deep Peat Bed, San Joaquin Valley, California (San Joaquin)*: Peat from well dug by Bureau of Reclamation near Tranquillity, California, in studying ground-water conditions of the San Joaquin Valley in connection with Central Valley Project. Peat found at depth of about 550 feet. A silty clay overlaid the peat, and a clay stone lay beneath it. The bed itself was about 1 foot thick. The flecks of wood were not replaced. The condition described prevails over an area of three townships in this vicinity, and the clay stone underlying the peat can be traced for at least 50 miles along the central part of the San Joaquin Valley. Age was desired to fix rate of deposition of the 500 feet of alluvial sediments on the valley floor. Donor's sample No. 15-16-12B. Submitted by E. F. Sullivan and Phil Dickinson, acting district managers, Bureau of Reclamation, Region 2, Fresno, California.	Older than 17,800
C-631	*California Crude I:* Crude oil taken from depth of 1100 feet in the Tulare formation of Upper Pliocene age at the South Belridge field in Kern County, California. This oil, together with that of No. C-632, is from the youngest productive horizons known to the Shell Oil Company. Submited by M. E. Spaght, Shell Development Company, Emeryville, California.	Older than 24,000
C-632	*California Crude II:* Crude oil from the Upper or Middle Pico formation of Upper Pliocene age, from the Padre Canyon field in Ventura County, California. The actual well was Hobson B 47-1 of the Chanslor-Canfield Midway Oil Company. This, together with No. C-631, constitutes the youngest crude oil samples measured. Submitted by M. E. Spaght.	Older than 27,780
C-659	*Indian Midden Shell, Lower California (Lower California Shell)*: Shell from Indian middens at Punta	1063 ± 160 716 ± 130

Our No.	Sample	Age (Years)
	Clara and vicinity in Lower California. Shells were cryptochiton. Harold C. Urey measured their temperature of formation to be 15° C. and concluded that no oxygen exchange of importance had occurred. Submitted by Carl L. Hubbs, Scripps Institution of Oceanography, La Jolla, California.	Av. 889 ± 100

C-673   *Medicine Lake Highlands, California* (*Medicine Lake*): A variety of hard pine found buried under the youngest pumice deposits of the Medicine Lake Highlands of northern California. This wood dates the final volcanic eruptions in this country and gives a maximum age for the huge flows of obsidian found in the vicinity of Medicine Lake. Submitted by Howel Williams, Department of Geology, University of California, Berkeley.

$\begin{cases} 1660 \pm 300 \\ 1107 \pm 380 \end{cases}$
Av. 1360 ± 240

C-689   *Hotchkiss Site, Contra Costa County, California* (*Hotchkiss*): Charcoal from the Hotchkiss mound in Contra Costa County (CCo–138). This was Burial 18. This site, which falls in the late Horison, is an important prehistoric village and figures prominently in the archeological sequence. Collected and submitted by Robert F. Heizer.

1229 ± 200

C-690   *Coyote Hills:* Charcoal from a refuse midden in the Coyote Hills site near Newark, Alameda County, California. This was Site Ala–328, and the midden was located in Pit 5A at the base of the culture deposits at a depth of 11 feet from the surface. The culture affiliation is middle Horizon, as defined by R. K. Beardsley in an article in *Am. Antiquity*, **14**, 1–28, 1948. Submitted by R. F. Heizer.

2588 ± 200
2090 ± 220
Av. 2339 ± 150

C-691   *Johnson Site:* Charcoal from the Johnson Mound Site near Sacramento, California, Sac–6, Trench Z, Excavation Unit 8, depth 36–40 inches. The charcoal sample actually came from a burned post imbedded in the floor of a house. This site is a late Horizon site, and the period covered by this culture has been assumed to be included in the last 1500 years. Submitted by R. F. Heizer.

2360 ± 400
2460 ± 165
Av. 2410 ± 200

C-695   *Big Sur, Monterey County, California* (*Big Sur II*): Charcoal from shell midden on California coast at mouth of Willow Creek about 30 miles south of Big Sur, Monterey County. Midden overlain by 10 feet of gravels. Present beach gravels submerge 4.5 feet of midden, indicating shore subsidence (cf. No. C-628 for another sample of charcoal from this midden; this date was 1879 ± 250). The charcoal in this sample

1840 ± 400

Our No.	Sample	Age (Years)

came from the base of the midden. Submitted by R. F. Heizer.

C-763
C-764
C-771
C-777
C-787
Rotten Modern Wood: The question of alteration of the radiocarbon assay by rotting and putrefaction processes was tested by measuring these samples, submitted by Ernst Antevs, The Corrale, Globe, Arizona. The modern world-wide assay on our counters is 6.68 counts per minute.

Assay

C-763	Dead branch from a live mesquite tree	6.73 ± 0.2 cpm
C-764	Same dead branch as No. C-763, but burned to charcoal	6.39 ± 0.5
C-771	The decomposed interior of a Gambel oak tree from Lakeside, Arizona	6.76 ± 0.17
C-777	The decayed center of a ponderosa pine	6.83 ± 0.12
C-787	Partly decomposed root of a ponderosa pine	6.73 ± 0.14

C-823   *Burnet Cave:* Charcoal from Burnet Cave, Guadalupe Mountains, Eddy County, New Mexico. The sample came from the 8–9 foot level in the fill of this cave. The sample should aid in determining the time of the extinction of the horse, the bison, the camel, the cave deer, the four-horned antelope, and the musk oxen in the southwestern region of the Great Plains. The animals found in this cave are northern forms which had been driven south by the advance of the Mankato ice sheet. The cave is described in Schultz and Howard, "The Faunas of Burnet Cave, Guadalupe Mountains, New Mexico," *Proc. Acad. Nat. Sci. Phil.*, **87,** 273 [1935]). The sample was collected in 1937 by E. B. Howard, R. M. P. Burnet, and Mr. and Mrs. C. Bertrand Schultz. Submitted by C. B. Schultz. 7432 ± 300

C-894
C-895
C-896
C-897
Searles Lake Mud (Searles Lake III, Searles Lake IV, Searles Lake V, Searles Lake VI): These materials came from Searles Lake, California. They consisted of organic extract from the mud which was obtained by extraction with acetone, evaporation to a thick syrup, and the precipitation of the resinous material by the addition of water. Submitted by W. A. Gale. The descriptions are as follows:

C-894   Extract representing the first foot of the parting mud seam between the upper and lower salt deposits of Searles Lake. This was taken at an average depth of 73.7 feet (73.2– $10,494 \pm 560$

Our No.	Sample	Age (Years)

74.2 feet. This sample should represent material deposited just prior to the last cessation of overflow of waters from the Owens Valley at the close of the last substage of the Ice Age (Tioga Age). Based on the accumulation of salines in Owens Lake since that time, this was estimated by the late Hoyt S. Gale (*U.S. Geol. Surv. Bull. 580-L* [1914]) to be about 4000 years ago.

C-895   Material from the 3.5-foot level of the parting mud seam, 76.2–77.2 feet in depth.   15,089 ± 1000

C-896   Material from the 7-foot level of the parting mud seam, 79.7–80.7 feet in depth.   18,000 ± 730

C-897   Bottom 1 foot of the parting mud seam. Depth of 82.8–83.8 feet. This sample should correspond approximately with No. C-615, which represented the bottom 2 feet of the parting mud seam in another location, and which gave an age greater than 16,000 years.   23,923 ± 1800

C-898   *Guano from New Cave, Carlsbad Caverns (Carlsbad)*: Guano material from the New Cave, Carlsbad Caverns National Park, New Mexico. It comes from a compacted layer of guano occurring in the silt fill of New Cave, Sec. 23, T. 25 S., R. 23 E., New Mexico Bureau of Mines. The layer is about 2 feet below the flowstone cap forming the present floor of the cave about 300 feet within and 50 feet below the cave entrance. The associated silt contains numerous skeletal remains of an extinct species of three-tailed bat, *Tadarida*. Dating affords a maximum age for the beginning of the maximum dripstone and flowstone development in New Cave. This is believed to have been contemporaneous with the same stage in adjacent Carlsbad Caverns 5 miles east. Submitted by Lloyd C. Pray, California Institute of Technology.   Older than 17,800

G. Nevada, Oregon, Utah, and Washington

C-221   *Gypsum Cave:* Dung of giant sloth from Gypsum Cave, Las Vegas, Nevada. Collected by M. R. Harrington in 1931 from Room 1, dung layer 6 feet 4 inches from surface. Submitted by M. R. Harrington through Ruth Simpson, Southwest Museum, Los Angeles.   10,902 ± 440
10,075 ± 550
Av. 10,455 ± 340

Our No.	Sample	Age (Years)
C-222	*Gypsum Cave:* Same from small room southwest of Room 1. Taken 2 feet 6 inches from surface.	8692 ± 500 8051 ± 450 8838 ± 430 *Av. 8527 ± 250*
C-281	*Leonard Rock Shelter, Nevada (Leonard Rock):* Unburned guano from layer containing wooden artifacts in Leonard Rock Shelter, Nevada (LRS2). Submitted by R. F. Heizer.	8443 ± 510 8820 ± 400 *Av. 8660 ± 300*
C-298	*Leonard Rock Shelter, Nevada (Leonard Rock II):* Atlatl foreshafts of hardwood (*Sarcobatus*, greasewood) from layer described in No. C-281. Submitted by R. F. Heizer.	7038 ± 350
C-554	*Leonard Rock Shelter, Nevada (Leonard Rock III):* Carbonized basketry from upper guano layer, Area C. Associated with infant burial. Submitted by R. F. Heizer.	2736 ± 500
C-554	*Leonard Rock Shelter, Nevada (Leonard Rock Baskets):* Another portion of the carbonized basketry found in Leonard Rock Shelter cave and represented by No. C-554, "Leonard Rock III," which gave 2736 ± 500. Submitted by R. F. Heizer. Comment: Earlier measurement must have been in error.	5779 ± 400 5694 ± 325 *Av. 5737 ± 250*
C-599	*Leonard Rock Guano:* Bat guano taken from immediately above the Pleistocene gravels in the Leonard Rock Shelter, Nevada. Submitted by R. F. Heizer.	11,199 ± 570
C-277	*Lovelock Cave, Nevada (Lovelock I):* Burned guano from preoccupation level, Lovelock Cave, Nevada (LC4A). Submitted by R. F. Heizer.	4448 ± 250
C-278	*Lovelock Cave, Nevada (Lovelock II):* Unburned guano, preoccupation level, Lovelock Cave (LC4B). Submitted by R. F. Heizer.	6046 ± 300 5961 ± 400 *Av. 6004 ± 250*
C-276	*Lovelock Cave, Nevada (Lovelock III):* Vegetal material, earliest occupation level, Lovelock Cave (LCB). Submitted by R. F. Heizer.	2452 ± 280 2517 ± 320 *Av. 2482 ± 260*
C-587	*Humboldt Cave, Nevada (Humboldt):* Basketry from Humboldt Cave in Nevada, excavated in 1936. This cave is some 10 or 12 miles west of Lovelock Cave. Submitted by R. F. Heizer.	1953 ± 175
C-247	*Mazama:* Charcoal from a tree burned by the glowing pumice thrown out by the explosion of Mount Mazama (this formed Crater Lake). This tree was found in a road cut above the Rogue River on Oregon Highway 230, about 10.5 miles toward Diamond Lake from the junction of Oregon Highways 230 and 62.	6389 ± 320 7318 ± 350 5938 ± 400 6327 ± 400 *Av. 6453 ± 250*

Our No.	Sample	Age (Years)

The pumice is about 75 feet deep at this point, and about 40 feet of pumice overlies the portion of the tree from which these samples came. The impression was that the tree was still in very nearly an upright position. Collected and submitted by L. S. Cressman, University of Oregon.

C-609 *Danger Cave, Utah (Danger Cave I)*: Charcoal, wood, and sheep dung from Danger Cave, near Wendover, Utah. Found on old beach of Lake Stansbury, consisting of 2 feet of sand deposited on cemented gravels. Both sheep dung and wood were found in the sand layer. Above this several feet of later deposits lie. This sample was sheep dung from donor's sample No. F 18 FS 535. Submitted by Jesse D. Jennings, University of Utah.

$11,453 \pm 600$

C-610 *Danger Cave, Utah (Danger Cave II)*: Wood only from same location as No. C-609.

$11,151 \pm 570$

C-428 *Fort Rock Cave, Oregon (Sandals)*: Several pairs of woven ropes sandals found in Fort Rock Cave, which was buried beneath the pumice from the Newberry eruption in Oregon. Though Cressman himself did not dig the sandals, he feels certain that the person who did gave the correct information. They are exactly like ones Cressman had dug but unfortunately had varnished, so that they could not be used for radiocarbon measurement. Submitted by L. S. Cressman.

9188 ± 480
8916 ± 540
Av. 9053 ± 350

C-430 *Catlow Cave, Oregon:* Organic debris from Catlow Cave No. 1 in Oregon. Taken from 2.88-foot depth (No. 1-3025). Submitted by L. S. Cressman.

$\begin{cases} 1118 \pm 190 \\ 798 \pm 230 \end{cases}$
Av. 959 ± 150

C-611
C-640
C-635
C-636
Danger (Lamus) Cave, Utah: Samples from Danger Cave near Wendover, Utah. Floor of cave has beach sand 2 feet thick from Lake Stansbury. This was dated at $11,453 \pm 600$ and $11,151 \pm 570$ by sheep dung and wood fragments, respectively, which were found in the sand (Nos. C-609 and C-610). Submitted by Jesse D. Jennings.

C-611 *Danger Cave III:* Charcoal from just above the sand in the lowest layers of the 15-foot deposit of garbage and debris found at the cave mouth. Donor's sample No. F 97 FS 515.

9789 ± 630

C-640 *Danger Cave VI:* Charred rat dung found on the sand. A thin layer of charred rat dung and ash was found at this level. Donor's sample No. FS 619 (Feature 18 or 19).

8960 ± 340

Our No.	Sample	Age (Years)

C-635 *Danger Cave VII:* Charred bat guano, plant stems, and twigs from 18–24 feet below the current surface of the pile of debris. Donor's sample No. FS 614 (Feature 17).   1930 ± 240

C-636 *Danger Cave VIII:* Charred bat guano, twigs, and plant fragments from 48–52 feet below the surface of the debris pile. Donor's sample No. FS 615 (Feature 5).   3819 ± 160

C-657 *Newberry Crater, Oregon (Newberry):* Charcoal from Newberry Crater, Oregon. Dates the final eruption of the volcano. The pumice covering the Fort Rock Cave (sandals, No. C-428) came from one or the other of the Newberry Crater cones. This shows whether the Fort Rock pumice is coeval with Big Pumice Cone and whether Newberry continued active after the great Mount Mazama eruption, which made Crater Lake. Charcoal from branches of wood up to 1 foot in diameter lying prostrate under a cover of 3–4 feet of rhyolytic pumice from the last pumice explosion within Newberry Crater. Found at new road cut between Paulina and East Lakes, 2.5 miles west of East Lakes Forest Camp and approximately 1.5 miles southwest of the vent of the Big Pumice Cone between the lakes. The exact spot was 0.1 mile west of the turnoff to Paulina Lake Summer Homes and the same distance east of the turnoff to the IOOF Camp. Submitted by Howel Williams.   2054 ± 230

C-728 *Lovelock Cave Basketry (Lovelock V):* Samples of
C-729 basketry to check the cultural type found in the
C-730 Lovelock Cave. Furnished by E. K. Burnett, Heye Foundation. Samples collected by Loud and Harrington and described in "Lovelock Cave" (*Univ. California Publ. Archeol. Ethnol.*, **25**, No. 1 [1929]). Submitted by L. S. Cressman.   1686 ± 220

C-728 Matting fragment, 18–48 inches below the surface.

C-729 Bulrush cud (*Scirpus validus*), 18–48 inches the surface.

C-730 Basketry fragments, 18–48 inches below the surface. These three samples were combined.

C-735 *Lovelock Cave Basketry (Lovelock II):* Basketry fragments from a depth of 96–126 inches below the surface in the same cave as described in Nos. C-728, C-729, and C-730. Submitted by L. S. Cressman.   3172 ± 260

Our No.	Sample	Age (Years)

C-827 *Lind Coulee, Washington (Lind Coulee):* Charcoal from an ancient occupation in site in the Lind Coulee. In this site stone artifacts are found in association with animal bones in deposits that have been identified by geologists as late Pleistocene in age. Among the bones from the site are those of bison. Because of the scrappy nature of the bones it has not been possible to identify the particular species of bison. The bones in general exhibit a fair degree of mineralization. Submitted by Richard Daugherty, State College of Washington.
$\begin{cases}9400 \pm 940 \\ 8518 \pm 460\end{cases}$
Av. 8700 ± 400

C-844 *Indian House Pit in Oregon (Klamath House):* Indian house pit on the Klamath Reservation, 18 meters long on the north-south axis, 16 meters wide on the east-west axis, and 2 meters in depth. A dead ponderosa pine in the house pit, which started its growth sometime after the abandonment of the house, seems to have lived about 250 years. Samples were wood taken from the house pit. Collected and submitted by L. S. Cressman.
430 ± 165

C-914 *Tule Springs Site, Tule Springs, Nevada (Tule Springs):* Ancient occupation site at Tule Springs. Excavated by Fenley Hunter and M. R. Harrington, Southwest Museum, Los Angeles. The sample consisted of charcoal taken from beneath one of the ash beds about 2 feet below the present surface and about 14 feet below the surface of the lake-bed deposit which at one time covered it It is thought that the charcoal is of human origin. Submitted by M. R. Harrington.
Older than 23,800

H. Minnesota, Wisconsin, and Wyoming

C-496 *Bronson, Minnesota (Bronson Interglacial):* Wood from a well, Bronson Station 1, 88 feet below surface in association with a wealth of plant material in a Preglacial spruce-tamarack forest. Collected by C. O. Rosendahl, Department of Botany, University of Minnesota (cf. *Ecology,* **29,** 291–96 [1948]). Submitted by W. S. Cooper, University of Minnesota.
Older than 19,000

C-497 *Moorhead, Minnesota (Moorhead Interglacial):* Wood from Moorhead Station 2, Minnesota, late Pleistocene. May be associated with early history of Lake Agassiz (cf. *Ecology,* **29,** 289–90 [1948]). Collected by C. O. Rosendahl and submitted by W. S. Cooper.
11,283 ± 700

C-334 *Minnesota Boreal (Boreal III):* Peat from Jackson Camp, Minnesota. Taken from 8-foot depth in Pol-
$\begin{matrix}7586 \pm 490 \\ 6866 \pm 350\end{matrix}$

Our No.	Sample	Age (Years)
	len Zone B (pine period) by J. E. Potzger, Butler University, Indianapolis, Indiana. Submitted by E. S. Deevey, Jr.	Av. 7128 ± 300
C-332	Minnesota Boreal: Peat from 8.5-meter depth in Cedar Bog Lake, Minnesota. Pollen Zone B. Collected by M. Buell. Submitted by E. S. Deevey, Jr.	7988 ± 420
C-308 C-365 C-366 C-536 C-537	Two Creeks, Wisconsin: Wood and peat samples from Two Creeks forest bed, Manitowoc County. Forest bed underlies Valder's Drift (Thwaites). Apparently the spruce forest was submerged, pushed over, and buried under glacial drift by the last advancing ice sheet in this region. Thought to be Mankato in age.	

Sample	Collection	
C-308 (spruce wood)	L. R. Wilson, University of Massachusetts	10,877 ± 740
C-365 (tree root)	J Harlen Bretz, University of Chicago	11,437 ± 770
C-366 (peat in which root [C-365] was rooted)	J Harlen Bretz, University, Chicago	11,097 ± 600
C-536 (spruce wood)	J Harlen Bretz and C. L. Horberg, University of Chicago. Collected several years later than Nos. C-308, C-365, and C-366 in 1950	12,168 ± 1500
C-537 (peat)	J Harlen Bretz and C. L. Horberg, University of Chicago. Collected several years later than Nos. C-308, C-365, and C 366 in 1950	11,442 ± 640 Av. 11,404 ± 350

C-504	Sand Island, Wisconsin: Peat from Sand Island, Bayfield County. This unique peat dates the one outlet stage of the Nipissing Great Lakes. Submitted by L. R. Wilson, University of Massachusetts.	3656 ± 640
C-419	Lake Butte, Wisconsin: Glacial wood (cf. Bull. Geol. Soc. Am., 54, 136 [1943]) found between Appleton and Menasha, on the eastern shore of Little Lake Butte des Morts. Log protruded from a sloping bank of varved clay, perhaps reworked but older than the surface till of Valder's Drift. Appears flattened by pressure. Collected and submitted by F. T. Thwaites, University of Wisconsin.	5938 ± 300 6864 ± 300 Av. 6401 ± 230
C-302	Sage Creek, Wyoming (Yuma): Partially burned bison bone with high organic content, from Sage Creek, Wyoming. Yuma site of Eisely and Jepsen. Submitted by G. L. Jepsen, Princeton University.	6619 ± 350 7132 ± 350 Av. 6876 ± 250

Our No.	Sample	Age (Years)
C-630	*Kimberly, Wisconsin (Neenah)*: Glacial wood from	10,676 ± 750

C-630   *Kimberly, Wisconsin (Neenah)*: Glacial wood from Kimberly, Wisconsin. This consisted of a tree stump approximately 9 by 5 inches, found about 12 years ago in an excavation at the Kimberly-Clark Paper Mill by workmen of the Lampert Company, of Oshkosh. Mr. Lampert gave pieces of the wood to the Oshkosh Museum. The mill is almost in a direct line with the Pointe Beach site of Two Creeks, and it is thought that it should be of Mankato age (cf. Nos. C-308, C-365, C-366, C-536, C-537, C-444, C-355, C-356, and C-337). James A. Lundsted, of the Oshkosh Public Museum, and Clifford Allen, of Kimberly-Clark, described the sample. W. F. Read, of the Department of Geology, Lawrence College, examined the site on May 2, 1952. He found that the wood occurred at a depth of about 10 feet in a section of varved clays 25 feet thick, which extends from the surface down to the limestone bedrock. He stated that the clay is "the youngest glacial deposit of the area" and "was almost certainly deposited in a temporarily ice-dammed lake formed against the front of the retreating Valders Ice (Lake Oshkosh)." According to C. L. Horberg, of the University of Chicago, this strongly indicates that the wood is of Mankato age and that it was deposited as driftwood in the Lake Oshkosh clays. Submitted by James A. Lundsted.

10,676 ± 750

C-668   *Keyhole Reservoir, Wyoming (Keyhole Reservoir II)*: Charcoal found in a small rock shelter (Site 48CK-204) that occupies the sloping shelf of the south side of the sandstone bluff west of Mule Creek and south of the Belle Fourche River. The rock shelter is known as Excavation Unit 2 (XU2). The sample was composed of seven small lumps of charcoal (Cat. Nos. 48CK204-120, -298, -327, -338, -430, -432, -462) and one lump of charred wood (Cat. No. 48CK204-429), taken from four basin-shaped, rock-filled hearths and from the sand matrix enveloping these hearths, and four similar hearths in squares N100E20 and L110E40 (XU2). A preliminary study of the data indicates that three components—two lithic and one ceramic ("Woodland")—are represented in XU2. Segregation of these components is difficult because the "floor" of the shelf is uneven, and the overlying deposits of fine wind-blown sand have been subject to inflation as well as deflation and have been profoundly disturbed by rodent action. Tentatively, two

2790 ± 350

hearth levels representing the earlier and later lithic components have been recognized. The charcoal and charred wood comprising this sample came from hearths and matrices of the "earlier" level. Four "McKean lancelate" fragments found below the level of these hearths and probably associated with them suggest that the earlier lithic components, XU2 may be contemporaneous with Level 1 in Site 48CK4 (No. C-667). Estimated age of the earlier lithic component, XU2, about 4000 years. Collected by Richard P. Wheeler and submitted by Paul L. Cooper, field director, River Basin Surveys, Lincoln, Nebraska.

C-667   *Keyhole Reservoir, Wyoming (Keyhole Reservoir I)*: Charcoal from a small rock shelter on the north side of the Belle Fourche River, about ¼ mile east of the Keyhole Dam. Sample was obtained from the matrix of Level 1, which was the lowest occupational stratum and lay directly on bedrock. It consisted of three small lots of charcoal (Cat. Nos. 48CK4-81, -103, -111), which were taken from squares numbered N100E15, N100E20, and N100E25. The number of the site is 48CK4. Together with the charcoal, fragments of small basally notched lancelate points (the "McKean lancelate" point) and other artifacts were found. These mostly resemble some material from Signal Butte IA. Collected by Richard P. Wheeler and submitted by Paul L. Cooper.

                $\begin{cases} 1660 \pm 250 \\ 1295 \pm 400 \end{cases}$
               Av. 1478 ± 200
               1813 ± 300
               Grand Av.
               1646 ± 200

C-702   *Muddy Creek:* Charcoal from an ancient hearth in a camp site found near the mouth of Muddy Creek, a tributary of the Big Horn River just above Boyson Dam, Wyoming. The material was found in Site 48Fr34 at the location NO37.3x EO36.6 in the Lower Level. The site is in the Shoshoni Basin. Submitted by William Mulloy, University of Wyoming.

               3540 ± 220

C-711   *Upper Muddy Creek II:* Charcoal from an ancient hearth found on Muddy Creek several miles above Site 48Fr34 (cf. No. C-702). The number of the hearth was 35, and the site is numbered 48Fr33. Submitted by William Mulloy.

               3350 ± 250

C-712   *Poison Creek:* Charcoal from a hearth found in an ancient camp site at the mouth of Poison Creek, a tributary of the Big Horn River just above the Boyson Dam in Wyoming. The hearth was No. 1 in Site 48Fr5. Submitted by William Mulloy.

               3506 ± 220

Our No.	Sample	Age (Years)
C-715	*Wind Creek:* Charcoal from a hearth in an ancient camp site found between Wind Creek and Mule Creek near the mouth of Mule Creek, which is a tributary of the Belle Fourche River just above Keyhole Dam in Wyoming. The site was 48Ck7, the hearth was No. 23, and the charcoal came from the Upper Level. Submitted by William Mulloy.	3287 ± 600
C-790	*Grasshoppers:* Grasshoppers found frozen in Grasshopper Glacier, Yellowstone National Park, Wyoming. They occurred well down toward the central and bottom portion and were removed and melted out by Irving Friedman of the U.S. Geological Survey. These grasshoppers were first reported in 1898 by Kimball. They are identified as *Melanoplus mexicanus mexicanus* (Sauss.), which is widely distributed and is the common grasshopper pest. In the 1870's and 1880's this species was particularly destructive on the Great Plains and in the northern Rocky Mountain region. It was very conspicuous because of pronounced migratory habits. In recent years it has migrated very little, presumably due to changing agricultural practices. The specimens preserved in the glacier apparently are of the migratory sort. Submitted by Irving Friedman.	45 ± 150
C-795	*Horner Site:* Charcoal from the Horner Site (Sage Creek Site), Park County, Wyoming (cf. No. C-302 which dated 6876 ± 250 years). This sample was collected in a heavily burned area which probably represented a hearth or fireplace. It was located in Square 9L-D. The site number is 48PA29. The Horner Site located near Cody, Wyoming, was a butchering site of the ancient Indians. By August 1950 about 180 bison skeletons had been recovered. Apparently the animals were slain in the fall of the year. The stone projectile points found in this site were of the Scotts Bluff and Eden types. Collected by the Princeton-Smithsonian Expedition in the summer of 1952. Submitted by Waldo R. Wedel.	6151 ± 500 7690 ± 850 *Av.* 6920 ± 500
C-722	*Red River Terrace I:* Carbon from Red River terrace located 1 mile northwest of Robbin, Kittson County, Minnesota; SE. corner, S. ½, irregular Sec. 19, T. 159 N., R. 50 W. Horberg locality No. 1. Collected by Lloyd G. Tanner and Cyril Harvey, September 10, 1951. Carbon collected from soil zone 20 feet 6 inches above water level. Submitted by C. B. Schultz.	2150 ± 400

Our No.	Sample	Age (Years)
C-723	*Red River Terrace II:* Carbon from Red River terrace located 1 mile northwest of Robbin, Kittson County, Minnesota; SE. corner, S. ½, irregular Sec. 19, T. 159 N., R. 50 W. Horberg locality No. 1. Collected by Lloyd G. Tanner and Cyril Harvey, September 10, 1951. Carbon collected from soil zone 18 feet 8 inches above water level. Submitted by C. B. Schultz.	2684 ± 200
C-800	*Appleton:* Pleistocene wood from Appleton, Wisconsin, SE. ¼ Sec. 28, T. 21 N., R. 17 E., found below plain of glacial Lake Oshkosh, imbedded in a diagonal position in clayey red Valders till. The bark still remained on some of the log. From this Professor Read of Lawrence College, who collected the material, concluded that the wood could not have been transported very far before burial. Associated deposits include preglacial lake silts and sand and gravel. It was identified as spruce (*Picea*) by L. R. Wilson, University of Massachusetts. It was found at a depth of 14 feet below the plain of Lake Oshkosh. Submitted by C. L. Horberg.	11,471 ± 500 10,241 ± 650 *Av. 10,856 ± 410*
C-836	*Old Copper, Oconto, Wisconsin (Old Copper I):* Charred wood from the Old Copper culture site near Oconto. The samples were directly associated with Archaic burials. The Old Copper culture has never been accurately dated. Charred wood from crematorium Feature 1, Area II. Submitted by Robert E. Ritzenthaler, Milwaukee Public Museum.	5600 ± 600
C-837 C-839	*Old Copper, Oconto, Wisconsin (Old Copper II):* Charred wood from Feature 3, Area I, constitutes No. C-837, and charcoal from Feature 11, Area I, constitutes No. C-839. Twelve grams of No. C-837 and 8 grams of No. C-839 were mixed and measured. Submitted by Robert E. Ritzenthaler.	7510 ± 600

I. South Dakota

C-454	*Angostura, South Dakota:* Charcoal from site in the Angostura Reservoir area. Horizontal zone 3.5 inches thick mixed with clay (decomposed Pierre Shale). Donor's sample No. 39FA65–203 from Square N7E4, Area B. Submitted by F. H. H. Roberts.	7715 ± 740
C-604	*Long Site, South Dakota:* Charcoal from the Long Site (39FA65) in the Angostura area of southwestern. The charcoal was taken from an oval-shaped unprepared hearth (Feature 14) 2.1 feet long and 1.5 feet wide in the west center of Square N3E3. Part also was	7073 ± 300

Our No.	Sample	Age (Years)

taken from a small surrounding area. Donor's sample No. 39FA65–417. Collected by Richard P. Wheeler in the summer of 1950 in the field party of Paul L. Cooper, River Basin Surveys, University of Nebraska. Submitted by Paul L. Cooper.

J. ALASKA

C-101 *Yukon, Canada (Johnson I)*: Charcoal and charred- 1606 ± 180
C-102 wood samples from buried soil layer in the Yukon. 1460 ± 180
C-112 Submitted by F. Johnson. *Av. 1533 ± 150*

C-260 *Ipiutak, Alaska (Ipiutak)*: Wood from the Ipiutak 973 ± 170
site at Deering, Seward Peninsula, Alaska. Third
level in debris. Estimated date A.D. 0–500. Excavated
by Helge Larsen, summer of 1949. Submitted by
F. Rainey.

C-266 *Ipiutak Alaska (Ipiutak II)*: Wood from Grave 51 at 912 ± 170
Ipiutak. Described in Larsen and Rainey, *Ipiutak
and the Arctic Whale Hunting Culture* ("Archeological
Papers of the American Museum of Natural History," Vol. **42**). Submitted by Helge Larsen, University of Alaska, College, Alaska.

C-409 *Pre-Aleut, Aleutian Islands (Aleut I)*: Charcoal from ⎰2920 ± 240
an Aleut village site near the village of Nikolski on ⎱3407 ± 520
Uniak Island. This particular sample was taken from *Av. 3018 ± 230*
a depth of 433 cm. and is a pre-Aleut in age. Submitted by W. F. Laughlin, University of Oregon.

C-299 *Fairbanks:* Wood found under 80–100 feet of frozen Older than
muck in the gold diggings near Eva Creek, Fairbanks, 20,000
Alaska. Submitted by Wendell Oswalt, University of
Alaska Museum, College, Alaska.

C-506 *Norton Bay, Alaska (Alaska II):* Charred wood from 1460 ± 200
middle levels, Iyatayet site, Norton Bay, Alaska.
Excavated by Giddings in 1949. Submitted by F.
Rainey.

C-563 *Denbigh, Alaska (Denbigh Log)*: Base log from Paleo- 2016 ± 250
Eskimo House 7–IYH7; Cape Denbigh, Iyatayet
site. Submitted by F. Rainey.

C-505 *St. Lawrence Island, Alaska (Alaska I)*: Spruce wood 2258 ± 230
from Hillside (Okvik House), Gambell, St. Lawrence
Island, Alaska. Excavated by Giddings in 1939. Submitted by F. Rainey.

C-560 *Trail Creek:* Willows and charcoal from 80-cm. depth 5993 ± 280
in Cave 9 at Trail Creek, Alaska. Submitted by F.
Rainey.

Our No.	Sample	Age (Years)

C-301 *Fairbanks Creek:* Wood from 30- to 60-foot depth on Fairbanks Creek, Fairbanks, Alaska. Associated with extinct mammal bones. Submitted by Wendell Oswalt.   12,622 ± 750

C-696 *Uyak Bay, Kodiak Island, Alaska (Kodiak Island):* Wood from refuse midden excavated by A. Hrdlicka in 1935 on Uyak Bay, Kodiak Island. Came from the permafrost ground in the midden. Submitted by R. F. Heizer.   333 ± 280

C-792 *Denbigh Flint I:* Charcoal from the Denbigh Flint Complex in the site at Iyatayet, Alaska. The layer from which the sample came was covered at the point of sampling by sterile sandy silt, a layer of peaty material, and then by silt loam containing "palae-Eskimo" and "neo-Eskimo" materials. The depth of the layer in this section was between 6.5 and 7 feet. The sample was scraped from the complex in place in Section IYZ–5B near the middle of the terrace. It was collected and submitted by J. L. Giddings, University of Pennsylvania Museum.   3477 ± 310
                   3541 ± 315
Av. 3509 ± 230

C-793 *Denbigh Flint II:* Charcoal from the Denbigh Flint Complex in the site at Iyatayet, Alaska (cf. No. C-792). The layer at this point was covered by 4.5 feet of soil including Eskimo materials above the usual sterile layer. This section, labeled "Section IYR," is high on the terrace slope where later cultural materials were thinly deposited. It is about 50 feet from the section in which No. C-792 was collected. Collected and submitted by J. L. Giddings.   4253 ± 290
                   5063 ± 340
Av. 4658 ± 220

IV. MEXICO AND CENTRAL AMERICA
(*Principal collaborator:* H. DE TERRA)

C-199 *Tlaltilco, Mexico (Mexico I):* Charcoal from various burials at different depths at Tlaltilco. Early to middle Archaic period. Collected by H. de Terra. Submitted by D. F. R. de la Borbolla, Museo Nacional de Antropología, Mexico, D.F.   3407 ± 250

C-196 *Zacatenco I, Mexico (Mexico II):* Charcoal from lowest sherd layer, associated with Zacatenco I pottery. Early Archaic period, refuse heap at Zacatenco, Mexico. Collected by H. de Terra. Submitted by D. F. R. de la Borbolla.   3310 ± 250

C-203 *Teotihuacán, Mexico (Mexico III):* Charcoal from core of Pyramid of Sun, Teotihuacán, Mexico. The sample was taken in an excavated tunnel 65–100   2434 ± 500
                   1519 ± 200
Av. heterogeneous

Our No.	Sample	Age (Years)

meters from entrance below main center staircase. The core of pyramid contains late Archaic type of pottery. Collected by H. de Terra. Submitted by D. F. R. de la Borbolla.

C-198   *Tlaltilco, Mexico (Mexico IV)*: Charcoal from pre-ceramic level including "Chalco culture" artifacts in Rio Hondo terrace gravels at Tlatilco. Collected by H. de Terra. Submitted by D. F. R. de la Borbolla.
     6904 ± 450
     6017 ± 320
     Av. 6390 ± 300

C-200   *Cuicuilco:* Charcoal from pottery level below Pedregal lava near pyramid of Cuicuilco. Associated with pottery and figurines of late Archaic (Qicoman phase type). Collected by H. de Terra. Submitted by D. F. R. de la Borbolla.
     2422 ± 250

C-202   *Loma del Tepalcate, Mexico (Loma)*: Charcoal from floor of stone structure, Loma del Tepalcate, late Archaic period. Collected by H. de Terra. Submitted by D. F. R. de la Borbolla.
     2565 ± 200

C-207   *Tamaulipas, Mexico (Pueblito)*: Charcoal from top level of Site T174, state of Tamaulipas. Excavated from Square N25, La Perra or Pueblito culture. Collected by R. S. MacNeish. Submitted by D. F. R. de la Borbolla through H. de Terra.
     505 ± 165
     990 ± 220
     Av. 651 ± 150

C-204   *Becerra Wood, Mexico:* Wood from Ciudad de los Deportes near Mexico City, Armenta Horizon associated with mammoth, horse, etc. Younger Becerra formation. Collected in 1944 by Arellano and H. de Terra. Submitted by D. F. R. de la Borbolla.
     Older than 16,000

C-205   *Becerra Peat, Mexico:* Peat from same station as No. C-204 but 500 meters east. Also from the Armenta Horizon. Collected in 1944 by Arellano and H. de Terra. Submitted by D. F. R. de la Borbolla.
     11,003 ± 500

C-421   *Marl at Tepexpán, Mexico (Tepexpán I)*: Stems and roots of aquatic plants extending from 48 to 70 inches from surface of marl into and through caliche layer beneath which fossil Tepexpán man was found. Collected and submitted by H. de Terra, Wenner-Gren Foundation, New York.
     3800 ± 450
     4430 ± 350
     Av. 4118 ± 300

C-422   *Atetelco, Mexico (Sun Temple)*: Charcoal from debris in south chamber of "painted patio," 1.40 meters above floor of patio. In association with Teotihuacán II style pottery. Submitted by H. de Terra.
     { 1878 ± 200
     { 2611 ± 330
     Av. 2244 ± 180

C-423   *Teotihuacán, Mexico (Sun Temple)*: Wood from large pillar on exhibit at Teotihuacán. Excavated 1921 in "Ciudadela" at Teotihuacán, probably part of sup-
     3424 ± 230

Our No.	Sample	Age (Years)

port for younger temple of Quetzalcoatl superimposed on older structure. Submitted by H. de Terra.

C-424 *Monte Negro, Mexico (Alban I)*: Charcoal from Temple X at Tilantongo, Oaxaca. Sample of collapsed roof beams of temple excavated with rubble from temple floor, Monte Alban I level. Submitted by Alfonso Caso, Instituto Nacional Indigenista, Mexico, D.F.

{ 2518 ± 250
{ 2680 ± 200
Av. 2600 ± 170

C-425 *Monte Alban, Mexico (Monte Alban II)*: Charcoal from Well of Offering No. 3, Mound II (Temporada XII), Monte Alban, Monte Alban II level. Submitted by Alfonso Caso.

2223 ± 145

C-426 *Chachoapan, Mexico (Alban III)*: Wood from roof beams in tomb at Chacoapan, District of Nochixtlán, Oaxaca. "Corresponds with pottery of Monte Alban III-A type." Submitted by Alfonso Caso.

1652 ± 185

C-687 *Tamaulipas, Mexico (Le Perra)*: Vegetable material from Cave Tm.c.174. This is from the same site as No. C-207, which gave 651 ± 150 years, but this sample is well below the earlier charcoal sample. It was associated with artifacts of the Le Perra culture—the pre-pottery horizon—and should be uncontaminated culturally and physically. It was taken from 16–22 feet below the surface in Square N10W5 at Level 6 by R. S. MacNeish, National Museum, Ottawa, Canada. Submitted by Mr. MacNeish.

4445 ± 280

C-799 *Guatemala:* Charcoal from a log at the base of a very thick deposit of pumice laid down by glowing volcanic avalanches in Guatemala. The material was collected by Edwin Shook, of the Carnegie Institution of Washington. It was found on the west edge of the highway between Patzun and Godinez, Department of Chimaltenango, above Rio Chocoyos at the 6000 foot level in Chocoyos Cañon in Guatemala. The sample was from a location near the bottom of a deposit of fine to thumb-size white pumice. It was 15 cm. in diameter and 8 meters long. The importance of the specimen is that it serves to date the colossal glowing avalanche deposit west of Lake Atitlan. Similar deposits probably of about the same age, to judge by their degree of erosion, are widespread north of Lake Atitlan, also in the great valley around Guatemala City, and in the valley extending west from Totonicapan and in the valley north of Quetzaltenango. In brief, many of the largest valleys of Guatemala were inundated to a great depth by these avalanches during post-Pleistocene times. It

Older than 16,000

Our No.	Sample	Age (Years)

is the opinion of Howel Williams that dating of the sample will serve to date, if only approximately, all the other valley fills. L. C. Stuart says the nonoccurrence of charcoal above this sample indicates that no major eruptions have occurred there since. Submitted by Howel Williams.

C-884 *Pre-Classic Miraflores, Kaminaljuyu, Guatemala (Guatemala I)*: Charcoal from Str. 4, Md. E-III-3, Kaminaljuyu. This belongs to the pre-Classic Miraflores phase in this area. Collected and submitted by Edwin M. Shook, Carnegie Institution of Washington.

3142 ± 240

C-886 *Pre-Classic Majadas, Kaminaljuyu, Guatemala (Guatemala IV)*: Charcoal from an intrusive cache of jades, pottery, and sculpture in Md. C-III-6, Kaminaljuyi. This belongs to the pre-Classic Majadas phase. Collected by Edwin M. Shook.

2970 ± 200

C-887 *Pre-Classic Miraflores, Kaminaljuyu, Guatemala (Guatemala III)*: Charcoal from Str. 5, Md. E-III-3, Kaminaljuyu. Sample from the fill of Str. 5, stratigraphically slightly postdating No. C-884. Miraflores phase (formerly Verbena) of the pre-Classic. Collected by Edwin M. Shook.

2490 ± 300

C-891 *Pre-Classic Eruption in El Salvador (El Salvador)*: Charcoal from San Salvador. Charcoal which serves to date the last pumice explosions of El Boqueron volcano and the pre-Classic artifacts (cf. Nos. C-884, C-886, and C-887) found in abundance in the same stratum at many localities in and near San Salvador. This charcoal comes from a well ¼ mile north of the Inter-American highway bridge over Rio Acelhuate, approximately 1 mile east of San Salvador. It occurs in a layer of humus-bearing weathered pumice and is overlain by 31 meters of fluviatile pumice. Collected and submitted by Howel Williams.

2993 ± 360

C-948 *Mayan (Mayan I, II)*: In the case of these samples
C-949 a second attempt to test the limit of sensitivity of the radiocarbon dating method was made. The first, published in the last date list (5), concerned samples from Nippur fixing the Babylonian calendar. The choice between the Spinden and Goodman-Thompson correlations for the Mayan calendar is the point at issue. In November, 1951, Kulp (*Science*, **114**, 565) published a single result on wood taken from a carved Mayan lintel from structure 10, Tikal. The carved

date on the lintel was 9.15.10.00 in the Mayan calendar, which, according to the Goodman-Thompson correlation, would be June 30, A.D. 741, and, according to the Spinden correlation, would be October 30, A.D. 481. Kulp's result was A.D. 481 ± 120.

The present samples from carved lintels from Tikal, Guatemala, were furnished from the Ethnographical Museum at Basel, Switzerland. No. C-948 was taken from the famous lintel shown on Plate 42 of Morley's *The Ancient Mayan*. It consisted of sapodilla wood and bore the Mayan date 9.15.10.00, the same as the sample tested at Columbia University. No. C-949 was taken from the glyphic of the lintel shown on Plate 72 (Maudslay). It bore the same date and also was sapodilla wood.

The samples were measured separately over a period of about 6 weeks in each case, and the mean results calculated. Within the experimental error of about 1 per cent, the net count rate for both samples agreed. Combining these data with the half-life of radiocarbon, which is estimated to involve an error of 0.54 per cent, and the assay for modern wood, which we take to have an error of 0.67 per cent, we obtain the results given. The samples were submitted by Hans Dietschy of the Ethnographical Museum, Basel. Most of the measurements were taken by Delia Gonzalez Tudge.

C-948   Date, A.D. 469 ± 120.   1485 ± 120
C-949   Date, A.D. 433 ± 170   1521 ± 170
Weighted average: Date, A.D. 451 ± 110.   1503 ± 110

V. SOUTH AMERICA

(*Principal collaborator:* J. B. BIRD)

C-321   *Huaca Prieta, Peru* (*Chicama*): A series of samples
C-318   from Huaca Prieta Mound 3, which is preceramic.
C-316   Collected and submitted by J. B. Bird, American
C-315   Museum of Natural History, New York.
C-313

Sample	Level (Depth in Feet from Top)	
C-321 (12) (plant material)	HP-D; 6	2966 ± 300
C-318a (9) (wood)	HP3-J2; 22	1989 ± 196
C-318b (9) (wood)		3550 ± 600
C-316 (7) (wood)	HP3-M; 30	4380 ± 270
C-315 (6) (shell)	HP3-M; 30	3572 ± 220
C-313 (4) (wood)	HP3-Q1; 36	4257 ± 250

Comment: First sample (No. C-318a) looks incorrect.

Our No.	Sample	Age (Years)
C-362	*Huaca Prieta, Peru (Chicama VII)*: Sample of cattail roots from Layer K-2 of Huaca Prieta Mound 3. Should be between Nos. C-316 and C-318. Submitted by J. B. Bird through H. C. Cutler, Chicago Natural History Museum.	4044 ± 300
C-598	*Huaca Prieta:* Charcoal from the lowest occupation level of Huaca Prieta Mound 2, found directly on bedrock by Constante Larco, under the direction of J. B. Bird. Submitted by J. B. Bird.	4298 ± 230
C-75	*Huaca Prieta, Peru (Peruvian)*: Algaroba wood from roof beam section of subterranean house found in Huaca Prieta Mound 5 at the level of first appearance of maize and Cupisnique pottery, Chicama Valley, Peru. Collected and submitted by J. B. Bird.	2665 ± 200
C-322	*Huaca Prieta, Peru (Chicama IV)*: Wooden digging stick from House No. 2 of Huaca Prieta Mound 5. Should be more than 100 years older than Cupisnique (No. C-75). Submitted by J. B. Bird.	$\left\{\begin{array}{l} 3278 \pm 250 \\ 3333 \pm 340 \end{array}\right.$ *Av. 3310 ± 200*
C-323	*Huaca Prieta, Peru (Peruvian Rope)*: Rope in excellent condition from cache in lowest layer (D) of Huaca Prieta Mound 1. Associated with early Negative (Gallinazo) pottery. Submitted by J. B. Bird.	2632 ± 300
C-382	*Moche:* Ash mixed with bone from Moche site at Huaca de Sol, northern Peru. Taken from habitation site, ground level, beneath pyramid on north face in center. Associated with Mochica sherds. Collected and submitted by G. Kubler, Yale University.	2823 ± 500
C-619	*Virú Valley, Peru (Mochica Rope)*: Rope from a late Mochica burial at Huaca de la Cruz in the Virú Valley. Associated pottery indicates it dates from the latter part of the Mochica period as recorded in the Virú, the first valley south of Moche. Submitted by W. D. Strong, Department of Anthropology, Columbia University, through J. B. Bird.	1838 ± 190
C-271	*Paracas Necropolis, Peru (Paracas)*: Cotton cloth from the mummy brought to New York in 1949 by Dr. Rebecca Carrion, National Museum of Anthropology and Archaeology, Peru. From Paracas Necropolis. Submitted by J. B. Bird.	2190 ± 350 2336 ± 300 *Av. 2257 ± 200*
C-460	*Nazca Valley, Peru (Nazca I)*: Sections of four darts, distal ends painted black, three hard and whipping at end. Cahuachi, Nazca Valley, Section Aj, Location A, Grave 10, Nazca A Period. Excavated by A. L. Kroeber. Specimen No. 171210, Chicago Natural History Museum. Submitted by D. Collier.	1314 ± 250

Our No.	Sample	Age (Years)

C-521 *Nazca Valley, Peru (Nazca II)*: Wood fragments of Atlatl shaft from Grave 12, Location A, Section Aj, Cahuachi, Nazca Valley. Nazca A Period. Catalogue Nos. 171245 and 171246. Should be contemporaneous with Paracas mummy. Collected by A. L. Kroeber and submitted by D. Collier.

$\{$ 1681 ± 250
$\{$ 2477 ± 200
Av. 2211 ± 200

Av. including No. C-460
1988 ± 200

C-378 *Chincha, Peru (Chincha)*: Guano from North Chincha Island found beneath 3 feet 6 inches of wind-borne sand at Quebrada del Panteon by G. Kubler. Submitted by Mr. Kubler.

Older than
19,000

C-484 *Mylodon Cave, Chile (Chilean Sloth)*: Dung of giant sloth from Mylodon Cave, Ultima Esperanza, Chile (51°35′ S.). Not associated with human artifacts, though sloth and man found together in three caves 125 miles distant (cf. No. C-485). There is an as yet undetermined correlation with the last ice advance in Patagonia. Submitted by J. B. Bird.

$\{$ 10,800 ± 570
$\{$ 10,864 ± 720
Av. 10,832 ± 400

C-485 *Palli Aike Cave, Chile (Chilean Bone)*: Burned bone of sloth, horse, and guanaco, associated with human bones and artifacts. Valuable in determining time of arrival of man at tip of South America. Material found in Palli Aike Cave, 125 miles east of Mylodon. Submitted by J. B. Bird.

8639 ± 450

C-658 *Nazca Valley, Peru (Nazca Wool)*: Dyed wool in the the form of a turban bandeau. Taken from Grave 13, Cahuachi, Nazca Valley, Peru, by A. L. Kroeber. It was at Location A and in Section Aj (cf. No. C-521). Submitted by D. Collier.

1679 ± 200

VI. TREE-RING SAMPLES

C-103 *Broken Flute Cave, New Mexico (Tree Ring)*: Douglas Fir wood excavated by Morris in 1931 from Red Rock Valley, Room 6, Broken Flute Cave. Inner ring A.D. 530; outer ring A.D. 623. Submitted by T. L. Smiley, Laboratory of Tree Ring Research, University of Arizona, Tucson.

973 ± 200
1070 ± 100
Av. 1042 ± 80

C-159 *Sequoia*: Wood from the heart of the giant redwood known as the "Centennial Stump" felled in 1874, with 2905 rings between the innermost (and 2802 rings between the outermost) portion of the sample and the outside of the tree. Therefore known mean age was 2928 ± 51 years. Submitted by E. Schulman, Laboratory of Tree Ring Research, University of Arizona, Tucson.

3045 ± 210
2817 ± 240
2404 ± 210
Av. 2710 ± 130

VII. OTHER AREAS

Our No.	Sample	Age (Years)

C-548   *Ubayama Shell Mound, Japan (Japanese):* Charcoal from Ubayama shell mound, about 10 miles west of Tokyo, Japan. Charcoal was part of structural remains in a house area in the bottom levels of the mound. Found in fall of 1948. Thought to be oldest house site in Japan. Submitted by Ralph D. Brown, 26 West Rustic Lodge Avenue, Minneapolis, Minnesota. Similar sample submitted by Lieutenant Colonel H. G. Schenck. This sample was not measured.
     4850 ± 270
     3938 ± 500
     Av. 4546 ± 220

C-603   *Ubayama Shell Mound, Japan (Late Jomon):* Charcoal collected by Father Groot from the early Late Jomon (Horinouchi Stage) horizon at the Ubayama shell mound (cf. No. C-548) in Japan. Submitted through H. L. Movius.
     4513 ± 300

C-580   *West Africa:* Carbonized wood from a late Upper Pleistocene deposit at Mufo, Angola, Portuguese West Africa, associated with a Lupembian stone blade (late Stone Age). Found on the eastern bank of the Luembe River (7°38' S.; 21°24' E.). Stratigraphy was gray-white sand at surface 2.50 meters thick. At the base of this the Lupembian (late Stone Age) backed blade was found in mint condition, unworn and associated with the carbonized wood measured. Next below the sand was a gravel layer 65 cm. thick; next a ferritized gravel layer 5 cm. thick; then a gravel layer identical with the second layer from the surface. This was 10 cm. thick and rested on the bedrock of mica schist. Submitted by J. Janmart, Museo do Dundo, Comparrhia de Diamantes de Angola, Dundo-Lunda, Angola, through H. L. Movius.
     11,189 ± 490

C-581   *West Africa:* Carbonized wood found 15 cm. down in the gravel layer underlying No. C-580. Submitted by J. Janmart through H. L. Movius.
     14,503 ± 560

C-540   *Hawaii:* Charcoal from earliest Polynesian culture in Hawaii. Found in Kiliouou Bluff Shelter, Kuliauaw, Oahu Island, by Kenneth P. Emory, Bernice P. Bishop Museum, Honolulu 17, Hawaii. Submitted by K. P. Emory.
     946 ± 180

C-600   *Australia A:* Aboriginal kitchen midden charcoal from Australia, taken from Goose Lagoon, western Victoria, on property called "Leura" east of Goose Lagoon. The midden was on the north side of the aeolianite region and toward its east end, about 15
     1177 ± 175

Our No.	Sample	Age (Years)

feet above the alluvium flat. Collected by Edmund D Gill, National Museum of Victoria, Melbourne. Submitted by H. L. Movius.

C-601   *Australia B:* Aboriginal kitchen midden charcoal from Australia, taken from Koroit Beach at Armstrong's Bay, northwest of Warrnambool, Victoria. Collected by Edmund D. Gill, National Museum of Victoria, Melbourne. Submitted by H. L. Movius. 538 ± 200

C-629   *Manchuria (Seeds):* Ancient Manchurian lotus seeds, still fertile. Collected by Ichiro Ohga in the Pulantien Basin of southern Manchuria in a peat layer presumably of Pleistocene age; uplift and erosion had exposed the layer on the walls of the Pulantien River Valley. Ohga germinated several hundred seeds, either filing the thick outer shell or soaking in concentrated sulphuric acid for 1–5 hours. Genus *Nelumbo*, similar to the Indian lotus *N. nucifera*. Submitted by R. W. Chaney, University of California, Berkeley. 1040 ± 210

C-613   *Zimbabwe, Southern Rhodesia (Zimbabwe):* Large log from the famous prehistoric site of Zimbabwe in Southern Rhodesia. Zimbabwe is a rather elaborate town built by the ancestors of the modern Bantu peoples of South Africa. Generally thought to date from the fourteenth or fifteenth centuries A.D.; it may date as early as the ninth century A.D., however. It was to settle this controversy that this sample was submitted by H. L. Movius. 1415 ± 160
 1344 ± 160
 1271 ± 260
 Av. 1361 ± 120

C-660   *Lonze Forest, Barotseland, Northern Rhodesia (Lonze Forest):* Charcoal from newly developed pit in the Lonze Forest, Barotseland, taken at the 5-foot level (4 feet 10 inches to 5 feet 3 inches). There was no evidence of tree roots, and it is believed that the charcoal was free from root contamination. Collected by J. Desmond Clark, curator, Rhodes-Livingstone Museum, Livingstone, Northern Rhodesia. Submitted by H. L. Movius. 3585 ± 260

C-661   *Barotseland:* Charcoal from newly developed pit in the Lonze Forest, Barotseland, taken at a depth of 10 feet to 10 feet 4 inches at the site from which No. C-660 was taken. No. C-660 dated 3585 ± 260. Collected by J. Desmond Clark, Livingstone. Submitted by H. L. Movius. 3210 ± 250
 4300 ± 500
 Av. 3500 ± 225

C-662   *Situmpa Forest, Machili, Northern Rhodesia (Situmpa Forest):* Charcoal from pits dug in the Situmpa For- 4078 ± 300

Our No.	Sample	Age (Years)

est, taken at the 5-foot level, which is tied with an archeological locality that represents the first definitely dated archeological horizon in this region. This should prove a clue as to the age of the Bantu penetration of Barotseland. Collected by J. Desmond Clark. Submitted by H. L. Movius.

C-663 *Chifubwa Stream Shelter, Solwezi, Northern Rhodesia (Rhodesian Nachikufan I)*: Charcoal from Chifubwa Stream Shelter in Solwezi. From the lowest 18 inches of an orange sand and the top 4–6 inches of a late Stone Age occupation layer containing an industry known as Nachikufan I. The sample is of considerable importance for establishing the absolute chronology for prehistoric man in southern Africa. Collected by J. Desmond Clark. Submitted by H. L. Movius.

6310 ± 250

C-669 *Chalan Piao Site, Saipan Island (Saipan)*: Oyster shell found 1.5 feet below the surface at the Chalan Piao Site, about $\frac{1}{2}$ mile inland from the shore line in the undisturbed, indurated sand beds that lie along the west coast of Saipan Island. Potsherds occurred at this level, and the deposition of the sherds and shell appears to have taken place previous to a 6-foot eustatic fall in sea level. Guess date, based on Godwin's dating of this fall on the southern English coast, is 3000–4000 years. The outer, slightly powdery surface of the shell was removed to leave a translucent interior. H. C. Urey measured the temperature of deposition to be 27.5° C. by the oxygen 18 content, which is identical with present ocean temperatures in this area. Since the shell would have been washed by fresh water, alteration would have drastically changed this apparent temperature by changing the oxygen 18 content. Dr. Urey therefore concludes that the oxygen had not been replaced in the shell. Consequently, we believe that the carbon has not been replaced, since each carbon atom is surrounded by oxygens in the carbonate ions. Submitted by Alexander Spoehr, Chicago Natural History Museum.

3479 ± 200

C-688 *Chaney Seeds:* Wood (*Torreya nucifera*) from a canoe found about 20 feet below the surface in Kemigawa in 1948. This site is 8 miles east of Tokyo. The interest in this wooden canoe stems largely from the fact that Dr. Ichiro Ohga found three viable lotus seeds (cf. No. C-629) associated with the remains of the canoe. In addition to the viable seeds, he found

3052 ± 200
3277 ± 360
Av. 3075 ± 180

Our No.	Sample	Age (Years)

many lotus receptacles. Ohga's discoveries were made in April, 1951. Submitted by R. W. Chaney.

C-697 *Lonze Forest, Barotseland, Northern Rhodesia (Kalahari)*: Charcoal from depth of 12 feet in the Kalahari Sand in a pit 8 feet in diameter in the Lonze Forest. The sides of the pit were scraped at 12 feet to expose the charcoal. It is not a continuous horizon. The charcoal was found in seven places. Variation in depth between the lowest and highest samples did not exceed 8 inches. Collected by J. Desmond Clark. Submitted by H. L. Movius.

6098 ± 300

C-721 *Blue Site, Tinian Island (Tinian Blue Site)*: Shell *(Tridacna)* from the Blue Site on Tinian in the Marianas Islands, from Test A at a depth of 1.9 feet. At this site a skeleton was found that exhibited yaws, according to T. Dale Stewart, of the United States National Museum. Yaws and syphilis probably are manifestations of related forms of spirochete. The Marianas skeleton, as bearing on the existence of yaws in the Pacific prior to the historic period, is thus relevant to the larger problem of the development and spread of both yaws and syphilis. In addition, the Blue Site is representative of the major prehistoric cultural manifestation, the *latte culture*, which persisted up to the sixteenth and seventeenth centuries. How far back it goes is not known. Dating the Blue Site should furnish evidence. The excavation was conducted under the direction of Alexander Spoehr as part of the Chicago Natural History Museum Expedition in 1949–50. Submitted by him for dating.

1098 ± 145

C-829 *Situmpa Forest Station (Barotseland)*: Check pit excavated in 1952 by J. Desmond Clark of the Rhodes-Livingstone Museum, Livingstone, Northern Rhodesia. Charcoal from depth of 2 feet 10 inches to 3 feet 4 inches in redeposited Kalahari sands. Associated industry includes shards of Stamped Ware pottery (Bambata variant), which is not believed to be as old as would be indicated by the 4078 ± 300 years (2126 B.C. ± 300 years) obtained for No. C-662. This pit was dug at some 5 yards distance from the first excavation to check the earlier date. Submitted by H. L. Movius on behalf of J. Desmond Clark.

1854 ± 220

C-830 *Lusu Village, Zambezi River (Lusu Village)*: Charcoal collected in what appeared to be a large hearth in Lusu Village, Zambezi River, Sesheke District,

2025 ± 230
2353 ± 180
Av. 2139 ± 150

Our No.	Sample	Age (Years)

Barotseland. Sample taken just above spot where shards of Stamped Ware pottery of a believed Rhodesian Wilton occupation were found. This is overlain by 2 feet 7 inches of redeposited Kalahari sands. The section is very clear; the charcoal layer averages just over 1 inch in thickness and extends for 8 feet along the face of the section. Age believed to be approximately the same as that of the 4- to 5-foot horizon at the Situmpa Forest Station Pit, Machili (No. C-829). Submitted by H. L. Movius on behalf of J. Desmond Clark.

C-831
C-832 *Hawaii (Hawaii I and Hawaii II)*: Charcoal and wood from Bowl Cave on uninhabited Necker Island, northwest Hawaiian Islands. Found in 1923 reportedly under 14 inches of sterile dust in association with stone artifacts of ancient Hawaiian type and thought to be contemporaneous with the ancient stone ruins on the island (see *Archeology of Nihoa and Necker* [Bishop Museum Bull. 53], p. 90).

C-831 $1\frac{1}{16}$-ounce charcoal stored in museum in tin can, 1923–51, in glass jar, 1951–53. Collected by W. Anderson and submitted by Kenneth P. Emory. — 166 ± 200

C-832 $2\frac{1}{16}$-ounce piece of *wiliwili* (cork) wood, kept in cardboard box in museum. — 0 ± 250

C-850 *Fossil Skull, Florisbad, South Africa (Florisbad I)*: Peat I from Florisbad site. The site lies approximately 25 miles due north of Bloemfontein, Orange Free State, Union of South Africa. The geologic stratification of this site is very marked. At a depth of 19 feet in the lowest peat layer, from which No. C-850 was taken, the Florisbad skull, *Homo (Africanthropus) helmei*, was discovered *in situ* and in association with many stone implements and numerous extinct species of animals, for example, horse, hippopotamus, pig, and antelope. Above the lower-lying layer are three other layers of peat dated in later samples. Submitted by H. L. Movius on behalf of A. C. Hoffman, National Museum, Bloemfontein, Union of South Africa. — Older than 41,000

C-851 *Florisbad Peat (Florisbad II)*: Peat II, lying 47 inches above the lowest-lying peat (No. C-850), and itself 13 inches in thickness at the Florisbad site. Submitted by H. L. Movius on behalf of A. C. Hoffman. — 9104 ± 420

C-852 *Florisbad Peat (Florisbad III)*: Peat III, lying 52 inches above Peat II, which in turn lies 47 inches — 6700 ± 5000

Our No.	Sample	Age (Years)
	above the lowest-lying Peat I at the Florisbad site. Submitted by H. L. Movius on behalf of A. C. Hoffman.	

C-911 *Bushman Paintings, South Africa (Bushman Paintings)*: A very good sample of charcoal from South-West Africa. It bears on a very important dating problem, namely, the question of the age of certain styles of the so-called Bushman paintings. The charcoal was found stratified in a cave deposit in direct association with ocher for making the frescos which fill the cave walls. H. Breuil is convinced that a measurement of these charcoals will provide a first direct indication of when the main group of these painting was executed. The sample was collected at a locality known as the Phillip Cave, which is near Ameib, southeast of the Erongo Mountains in the Windhoek region of South-West Africa. Submitted by H. L. Movius on behalf of H. Breuil, Paris.
3368 ± 200

C-917 *Zimbabwe, South Africa (Zimbabwe II)*: Wood from an excavation in the "Temple" at Zimbabwe by K. R. Robinson in 1951 (see plan opposite p. 23 in *Zimbabwe Guide*). The specimen is cut from a second lintel, the first having already been dated at 1361 ± 120 years (No. C-613). Sample submitted by Hallam L. Movius on behalf of Roger Summers, National Museum, Bulawaya, Southern Rhodesia. This date was averaged with the date for No. C-613 of 1361 ± 120 to give a date of A.D. 574 ± 107 for the Zimbabwe city on the Christian calendar.
1506 ± 305

C-924 C-925 C-926 C-927 *Cave of the Hearths, Potgietersrus, South Africa (South Africa I, South Africa II, South Africa III, South Africa IV)*: Organic material from the ashy substance constituting the deposit in the Cave of the Hearths, South Africa. Collected by R. J. Mason. Submitted by K. P. Oakley, British Museum, London.

C-924	Middle Stone Age III; 130 in. in column "A"	11,600 ± 700
C-925	Middle Stone Age IV; 180 in. in column "B"	15,100 ± 730
C-926	Middle Stone Age II; 156 in. in column "A"	16,811 ± 960
C-927	Middle Stone Age I; 288 in. in column "C"	11,700 ± 610

CHAPTER VII

REFLECTIONS UPON THE SIGNIFICANCE
OF RADIOCARBON DATES

By FREDERICK JOHNSON

ARCHEOLOGISTS, geologists, and pollen analysts are continually searching for the means of improving methods of counting time. The commonly available relative chronologies lack precision, and it is impossible to correlate them with the calendar, except when they may be checked with written records or with more definite methods of counting time; for example, the calendar based on tree-ring counts. The latter methods, however, have regional and temporal limitations. Despite such difficulties, dates of varying reliability can be assigned to all major events and a large proportion of minor ones included in the subject matter of the several fields. The error in these dates varies from ± 150 years or less, as those of the Near or Middle Eastern civilizations, where written records supplement archeological data, to geological estimates of Pleistocene events the errors of which are often ± 30 per cent or more.

When first developed by Dr. Libby, the radiocarbon method promised to become a valuable research tool, improving our knowledge of chronology. This promise has been amply fulfilled. About two thousand determinations have been listed in the dozen or more publications from Dr. Libby's and other laboratories.[1] The ages range from a few hundred years to more than thirty thousand years. The dated samples have come from several parts of Europe and Africa, the Near East, Oceania, and North, Middle, and South America. Samples from the Arctic and the tropics as well as those from a wide variety of intervening environmental zones have been

1. In addition to the preliminary list published by Libby in 1950 and the five lists in *Science* which are given in chapter vi, the following lists have been published: Anderson *et al.*, 1953; Griffin, 1952; Johnson, 1951; Kulp, 1952; Kulp *et al.*, 1951; Kulp *et al.*, 1952; Ralph, 1955; and Suess, 1954.

dated. It is apparent that there is in existence the basis for a chronology which is world wide in scope. Perhaps the unique usefulness of this chronology, in addition to its scope, is the fact that the dates have been determined by a single method, and, without exception, they are directly comparable. Of great significance also is the ability to collate chronologies in several fields. The determination of the dates is independent of hypothetical geological, archeological, or analogous interpretations. Chronological problems which are interdisciplinary in nature can be solved by a direct approach.

The preliminary lists of dates distributed by Libby previous to 1952 raised a number of questions because the indicated ages of some significant events were of an appreciably different magnitude than the current ideas concerning them. In fact, the periods covered by several sequences were not at all concordant with opinions concerning chronology. These circumstances were responsible for a discussion of the validity of the results of the method, and, significantly, much re-examination of the basis for archeological and geological chronological opinions. Out of this has come general recognition, occasionally qualified, of the validity of the method. The body of data contributing to the proof of validity of the method is now large and convincing in spite of instances where claims for inaccuracy have been made. Though not always published, the data continue to accumulate because, in addition to the investigation of specific problems, it is necessary to measure and remeasure contemporary samples and those of known age in order to test and calibrate equipment. The correspondence of predicted to observed radioactivities in a number of samples of known age (Fig. 1) is a primary indication of validity. Supplementary to this are measurements by two laboratories on sections of sequoia trees. The results are comparable to the dates determined by tree rings. Significant, though indirect, evidence is the overwhelmingly large proportion of dates which are accepted as accurate. One may also refer to the number of dates which, though they are in the order established by stratigraphy, do not correspond with some present ideas of magnitude. Consistency is also significant. It may be clearly seen, for example, in measurements made by different laboratories on identical samples. The results are identical; in fact, we are not aware of a single significant disagreement. There have been a number of experiments to test various questions and to allay certain doubts concerning accuracy. As an example we note one of these, the testing of rotten wood at the suggestion of Dr. Ernst Antevs (Nos. C-763, C-764, C-771, C-777, and C-787). The results varied from 6.39 ± 0.5 to 6.83 ± 0.12 counts per minute. These are to be compared with 6.88 counts for modern world-wide assay.

It has been customary procedure to compare historical, geological, and archeological measurements of time with the radiocarbon measurements for the purpose of judging validity of any measurement but with particular emphasis upon radiocarbon results. Broadly, the procedure is justifiable, but there are significant objections to most conclusions which have been drawn from comparisons of details. The problem is to find a basis for comparison. Historical data, that is, measurements of time based upon a calendrical system and dependable written ethnohistoric record, appear to be directly comparable with the results of the radiocarbon method as expressed in number of years before the present. In other words, dates in both systems are referable to a single method of counting time. This is not true of geological and archeological measurements, except in relatively rare instances. Measurements of time in these fields are inferred from processes, the rates of change or progress of which are not constant and which are, as yet, quite unpredictable. There is no known standard rate for any one of these processes, and measurements of time for one process are invariably relative to rates of progress in other processes. It should be quite clear that inferred or relative dates of this kind and chronological frameworks made up of them are not standards of sufficient precision for judging in detail the validity of the radiocarbon dates. It is a matter of historical record that archeological sequences which have not been controlled by some method of counting time, such as tree-ring dating, have been assigned longer or shorter periods of time as various opinions waxed and waned in popularity or as new data were presented. Similarly, in geology several different chronologies for the Pleistocene are variously based and have reputable proponents who are fully cognizant of both the strength and the weakness of their position. In view of this it is obvious that conclusions regarding the validity or error in a single date or a sequence of radiocarbon dates must be drawn with extreme care.

There are a few geologists and archeologists who are skeptical of the validity of all or a large portion of the results. The larger group of scientists which question specific dates, or sections of sequences of them, are probably closer to the actual fact. That is, some radiocarbon dates do not indicate the age of the phenomena described for the samples, even though such dates represent true determinations of the quantities of radiocarbon in the samples. In such cases, judgment concerning accuracy of dates is not a simple task in which currently held hypotheses of a single field or of several fields can be used as proof. There are several factors which require careful consideration before a truly sound judgment can be made.

The physicists and chemists involved in the laboratory research are fully aware of certain constant errors in the method. Dr. Libby and others have discussed the character and size of these internal errors in some detail in earlier chapters.[2] In view of this we may base our present remarks upon the virtual certainty that errors in the method are not of an order which affects the accuracy or seriously limits the use of the dates.

An important source of error can be described as curatorial. Experience has shown that it is essential to exercise great care in cataloguing and storing samples for measurement. A perusal of the lists of dates also shows that controversy is likely to arise over dates on samples which were not specially collected for radiocarbon measurement, particularly samples which have been stored in museums or laboratories for several years or more. Perhaps the most extreme examples of this are the dates on Tchefuncte and Hopewell samples (Nos. C-126, C-237, C-239, C-150, and C-151). In the light of present knowledge such samples would probably not now be measured. Another curatorial problem is prevention of contamination by noncontemporaneous C^{14}. For example, sterilization to prevent fungal action is advisable, if not sometimes essential. Prevention of mixture with other samples and exposure to dust or other contaminants are obvious precautions, but they are really important if an accurate measurement is to be made.

An analysis of so-called "invalid" dates reveals that a very large proportion of them have been determinations on samples the source of which is questionable. An important source of errors of this kind

2. See chaps. ii and iii.

is contamination by noncontemporaneous root hairs, fungal action, or some analogous process. That such contamination is present in a sample is due either to unknown or to unsuspected factors which are not observed by the collector. As an example of this kind of error, we have the temerity to mention the dates on the Denbigh Flint Complex of Alaska, Nos. C-792 (3509 ± 230 years) and C-793 (4658 ± 220 years). For reasons which are as yet impossible to explain, many dates on archeological samples from Alaska are questionable. The same factors may also affect the Denbigh samples; nevertheless, archeological correlations indicate that the Denbigh Flint Complex is older than the material at Trail Creek, No. C-560 (5992 ± 280 years), and also other material presumably of similar age. Geological correlations in Alaska permit two estimates of age for the Denbigh Complex: "More than 12,000 years (earlier than 10,000 B.C.)" and the favored one, "8500 years (6500 B.C.)."[3] Added to this is the fact that, should the present radiocarbon dates be correct, adjustments in the timing of many events in much of northern North America will be necessary. While there is nothing precise or even stable about the archeological correlations and the geological estimates, the evidence that the radiocarbon dates on the Denbigh Complex are erroneous is strong. The reason for the error can probably be traced to the character of the deposit. Illustrations and descriptions indicate that the layer was very thin and that it had been covered and folded during a cold period subsequent to its occupation. The charcoal comprising the sample was scraped from the thin layer through which noncontemporary, possibly even modern, roots had grown. Such circumstances render the dates extremely unreliable indicators of the age of the Denbigh charcoal. This is not due to the method of dating. It is possible that satisfactory dates might have been determined had the samples been collected with extraordinarily meticulous care and subjected to specialized cleaning and testing in the laboratory.

In some instances, certain dates have been declared invalid, and, more rarely, whole sequences have been repudiated because they are not in agreement with hypotheses concerning chronology based on other kinds of evidence. In such cases, it is necessary to examine closely the character and the degree of reliability of the evidence

3. Hopkins and Giddings, 1953.

before the radiocarbon dates may be rejected. This is difficult to do because it sometimes involves questioning the basic tenets of a field of investigation.

The time scales used by geologists, pollen analysts, and archeologists are, with rare exceptions, based upon stratigraphic sequences. Dates given in numbers of years for levels in a stratification can be misleading. With some exceptions, such dates are but convenient ways to indicate the estimated age, and a relatively large probable error is implied if not stated. Actually a date from one level indicates only its relationship to those above and below. The location of samples in a series of levels in the ground or distributed over historically identifiable surfaces of the earth establishes chronological relationships among samples. Knowledge of the extent of this relationship varies with the character of subsidiary information which may be derived from a study of the characteristics of several levels. As has been said so often, materials from the lowest strata are older than the materials from higher ones, provided of course that the whole deposit has not been overturned or otherwise disturbed. It may be added that, where superimposition is not directly observable, it may often be accurately deduced, thus placing in sequence nonoverlapping strata which may even be located in areas widely separated horizontally. Although general principles governing such deductions are commonly known, there are instances, often due to lack of fact, where chronologies based upon series of strata vary in degree of accuracy.

An adequately documented relative chronology of a sequence of geological or archeological events can be relied upon at the very least to indicate the order of events. Frequently reliable inferences concerning relative time intervals between events may also be made. However, when it is necessary to correlate events in one such sequence with those of another, inferences of contemporaneity or succession must be made with care. Such are not dependable unless supporting evidence indicates strong probability. In the earth sciences (archeology, etc.) such inferences are frequently made, and at times they are highly useful when properly considered. Regardless of these difficulties with relative chronologies, provable and in large measure, inferred sequences supply a background for the determination of chronology even though the results are not precise in terms of a limited number of years in the Christian calendar.

There are at least several kinds of problems in archeology. One involves especially the older remains of man where archeological materials can be assigned relative dates of varying degrees of reliability through collaboration with geology, pollen analysis, and other overlapping fields. The second is more frequently concerned with later cultural material found in situations having physical characteristics which are almost wholly due to the fact of human occupation. In such locations stratification is present, but it is frequently impossible to identify it. Consequently, archeologists augment scarce, definite stratigraphic data with inferences from internal evidence, such as the evolution of styles of pottery, changes in the form of tools, the shape of houses, etc. The resulting chronological framework is of course very insecure and is recognized as such by any reputable archeologist. The use of such must strain the credulity of investigators in allied fields, especially those in possession of more precise data. Be all this as it may, certain points in the relative time scale for recent human development in North America have become rather firmly established, not perhaps by logical proof, as in exact science, but by the sheer weight of confirmatory evidence. In other words, the probability of their accuracy is so strong that the possibility of error is slight indeed. Unfortunately, no suitable statistical expression of this can be made. Other dates, "guess dates" they are called in archeological jargon, are subject to controversies. These cannot be resolved at the present time, but they may be reduced by a process of elimination so that either ranges of error of these dates or hypothetical and sometimes multiple locations upon a time scale may be postulated. It is inevitable that further archeological research will bring to light evidence which will remove much of the uncertainties from these estimates.

It must be emphasized that, in spite of the lack of precision in all cases, many dates derived from purely archeological or geological phenomena are based upon evidence the validity of which is at present impossible to refute. It may be observed that, in instances where various types of evidence lead to real conclusions concerning chronology, the radiocarbon dates are in general agreement. Where the major difficulty actually appears is in situations where geologists or archeologists do not agree among themselves. In view of the nature of the data and the character of the material with which scientists dependent upon stratigraphy have to work, such disagreements are inevitable, and only meticulous, continuing analysis can reduce them. Nevertheless, basing statements concerning the accuracy of radiocarbon dates upon data which are in themselves controversial gives rise to incorrect and misleading conclusions or opinions. For example, in both archeology and geology it has been held that several sequences of radiocarbon dates do not allow enough time for specific series of events to take place. The actual expression of the idea is often obscured by complicated cross-reference to specific details and the couching of arguments in the current jargon. In geology, some but by no means all criticisms of the radiocarbon dates are based upon inferences concerning the behavior of a presently nonexistent ice sheet. There is no way of proving or disproving assumptions concerning the speed of advance or retreat of the ice, the degree of precision of a varve record and its correlation with the calendar, or the significance of the modifications in the vegetation. In various ways, these factors have provided useful opinions concerning the passage of time, such being based upon the weight of the evidence rather than upon observable fact. Similarly in archeology, opinions concerning time, when not based upon geological observations, are based largely upon assumptions concerning the rate of change in cultural processes. These are deduced from many sources, such as study of contemporary primitives, complicated comparisons and collations of sequences of events, etc. These opinions have varied greatly through the years, and no way of stabilizing them has yet been devised. Certainly a minimum of cogitation of the basis of some criticism of radiocarbon dates reveals the absurdity of it.

This leads us to observe that in many instances the location of samples providing unsatisfactory dates is incorrectly interpreted. The sample does not represent the event which the description says it does. This is quite frequent and understandable in situations where stratigraphy must be inferred from deposits widely separated horizontally. Another source of confusion is the incorporation in the deposit, in any one of several ways, of materials which are not contemporaneous with its development. Such sources of disagreement between radiocarbon and other dates are now being recognized. Revisions of opinion concerning the assignment of the sample is of course justifiable, and certainly the radiocarbon date may figure importantly in the modification of these opinions. However, it is equally certain that such modifications of opinion must be based upon stratigraphic or other sequential information.

The preceding comments outline a conviction that, within known limits, the method determines the age of samples which have been properly collected. However, it is necessary to subject all dates to critical interdisciplinary evaluation before they can be fully accepted. This involves meticulous examination of the process of collection and description of the sample and the standards upon which judgment is based. Gordon R. Willey has compiled a critique of archeological problems and radiocarbon dates in South and Middle America which is an excellent example of evaluation of a wide range of dates, including opinions concerning the significance of the chronological information.[4] A brief of the salient points and comments hardly does the work justice. Willey's essay is concerned with four obvious and basic problems. First, when did man enter Middle and South America? And how do the dates of his entry compare with his first appearances in North America? Second, when and where are the beginnings of American agriculture? And, as a corollary to this, what was the effect of domesticated food plants upon the growth of culture? Third, at what time and when did American cultures attain what might be called a Neolithic—or Formative—threshold, this threshold being characterized by stable village life based upon agricultural food production? Fourth, when did the Classic cultures —the "high" civilizations of Middle America and Peru—assume definite forms? And what was the duration of their existence?

Of the very few dates on "Early Man" in Latin America, the one of greatest significance comes from the Straits of Magellan. This date, 6688 ± 450 B.C. (No. C-485), is only 1000 years later than the Lubbock Folsom date (7932 ± 350 B.C. [No. C-558]) and implies man's early dispersal throughout the two American continents. In the valley of Mexico, the Younger Becerra geological formation dates from 9000 to at least 14,000 B.C. (Nos. C-204 and C-205). A lithic industry known as the San Juan has been associated with this

4. Willey, 1954.

formation. However, the above dates do not pertain to the cultural material. The Chalco lithic complex is found in a stratum overlying the Becerra, and a date on the complex, 4440 ± 300 B.C. (No. C-198), is consistent with the local stratigraphy. The few early radiocarbon dates available indicate that man entered Middle and South America not long after he became established in North America. This is expectable and does no violence to recent archeological conceptions.

Early and primitive races of maize from the simple La Perra culture in Tamaulipas, Mexico, have been dated at 2494 ± 280 B.C. (No. C-687). At Bat Cave, New Mexico, six levels have been dated, the earliest being 3981 ± 310 B.C. (No. C-573). Races of maize, as primitive as the La Perra maize, are probably not so old as the above but date from a middle-level reading about 2500 B.C. The great importance of these dates is that they are associated with the appearance of a domesticated food plant on an otherwise "early Lithic" stage of development and that they demonstrate the passage of a good many centuries without appreciable culture change. Undoubtedly, maize was a dynamic force in the rise of New World civilizations, as has been thought. However, contrary to the idea that it caused a sudden change in rate of development, maize appears to have played its role apparently without dramatic suddenness.

From Peru, a series of dates on the great refuse heap at Huaca Prieta have been discussed in detail by Bird.[5] Willey points out that the beginnings of an economy based on marine foods, gathering, and domesticated plants may be seen about 2348 ± 330 B.C. (No. C-598). This is roughly equivalent to La Perra. However, Peruvian agriculture of this time lacked maize; only domesticated roots and a local bean were cultivated. The other dates at Huaca Prieta are reasonably consistent with the stratigraphy. They indicate the first appearance of plain pottery between 1200 and 1000 B.C. In the near-by Virú Valley the radiocarbon dates for the early Guañape culture, characterized by plain pottery, is slightly earlier, 1149 ± 200 B.C. and 1849 ± 150 B.C. (L-122c, L-122f).[6] It is important to note that the above dates are determined from charcoal. Dates on

5. Bird, 1951.

6. Kulp *et al.*, 1952.

shell appear to be uniformly too early. A well-developed ceramic complex and domesticated maize is found in the following middle Guañape of Virú and is dated 1199 ± 90 B.C. (L-122a).[7] In view of various archeological correlations, this date is rather too early. The equivalent of this in the coast Chavin complex, called "Cupisnique," is dated 715 ± 200 B.C. (C-75). It should be noted that the Cupisnique pottery and stylistic complex appears fully developed; its arrival, coincident with maize, suggests outside influences with a long previous history elsewhere.

As was the case with Middle America, the Peruvian radiocarbon dates on agricultural beginnings were earlier than had been anticipated, but their acceptance necessitated no major revisions in chronological alignments. In both areas domesticated plants are recorded as far back as 2500 B.C., or earlier, and these plants are products of rather simple, preceramic cultures which undergo relatively little change for several centuries. There is another parallel in the abrupt appearance of a full-fledged Formative type culture—Cupisnique on the Peruvian coasts—and the Pueblito pottery-agricultural period in the Tamaulipas Highlands. The significant difference between early agriculture in Peru and Middle America is the much greater age of maize in the latter area.

About ten dates on samples from various levels of the Formative, or "American Neolithic," culture are not out of line with tenable ideas concerning correlation of materials in the valley of Mexico and the Guatemalan Highlands. At this stage, say, from about 1500 B.C. on to the younger dates determined, changes and developments in the highly organized groups were rapid. Variations or lack of precision perhaps, amounting to 100 years more or less in the dates, to say nothing of large counting errors, are sometimes difficult to accommodate in the short space of time available. In the present instance, however, adjustments because of the ranges are remarkably few.

As Willey observes, the dates indicate that a fully developed Formative culture was under way as early as 1500 B.C. in the valley of Mexico and, probably, elsewhere. A terminal horizon for the Formative is established by the various proto-Classic dates which fall between 700 and 200 B.C. (e.g., Nos. C-422, C-426, L-113,[8]

7. *Ibid.*   8. Kulp *et al.*, 1951.

C-948, C-949, C-460, C-531, and C-685). Formative cultures have been pushed back some 1500 years earlier than estimates of a decade ago. This lengthening of the Formative time span downward agrees, of course, with the early dates for American agriculture in the preceding incipient agricultural or Preformative stage. At the other end of the scale, however, the Middle American archeologist runs into his first real difficulty with radiocarbon—the surprisingly early termination of the Formative cultures and the corresponding lowering of the beginnings of Classic civilizations. In Peru, in general, the range of dates for the Formative is consistent within itself, although there are some surprises. Notable among these is the relatively early date for the very late Formative Gallinazo culture (682 ± 300 B.C. [No. C-323]) and Paracas Necropolis (307 ± 200 B.C. to A.D. 250 ± 250 [Nos. C-271 and L-115]).[9] Gallinazo is known to be not only later than Cupisnique (ca. 700 B.C.) but to be separated from it by another substantial period, the Salinar.

For the most part the Peruvian dates are appreciably later than those of the Middle American early Formative and suggest that the formative threshold was significantly earlier in Middle America than in Peru and that Middle American culture between the centuries of 1000 and 600 B.C. may have been the source for maize, developed ceramics, and temple-mound construction in Peru.

Classic civilization in central Mexico and Oaxaca has two radiocarbon dates which are consistent with previous archeological chronology as well as with the dates in the Formative in these regions. The dates 294 ± 180 B.C. (No. C-422) for Teotihuacán II is a little far from but not irreconcilable with the date A.D. 298 ± 185 (No. C-426) for Monte Alban III-A. The archeological cultures are assumed to be contemporaneous and are considered to be early Classic. Another Teotihuacan date, 1474 ± 230 B.C. (No. C-423) is, obviously, in error. Of extreme interest are dates on lintels of temple doorways from the late Classic Maya site of Tikal. The lintels have Maya dates which in the Spinden correlation are translated as A.D. 481 and in the Goodman-Thompson correlation as A.D. 741. The radiocarbon dates are amazingly close to the Spinden correlation, being A.D. 481 ± 120 (L-113),[10] 469 ± 120 B.C. (No. C-948), 433 ± 170 (No. C-949). The continuation of

9. *Ibid.*   10. *Ibid.*

the Classic Maya to a terminal date of about A.D. 650 may be accomplished by employing the Maya calendar. Thus there may be suggested a range of the Middle American Classic from the last centuries B.C. to A.D. 650 or a few hundred years earlier, as is indicated by archeology, in areas outside the lowland Maya area. Dates on Classic Mochica on the north coast of Peru and on Classic Nasca from the south coast create an over-all impression that Peruvian Classic cultures were, roughly, contemporaneous with those of Middle America; that is, beginning in the late centuries B.C. and continuing up through the first half of the first millennium A.D.

It is this time span of the Classic civilizations, as indicated by radiocarbon dates from both Middle America and Peru, that has come as the greatest surprise to most archeologists. Pushing back the beginning of the Classic and the relatively early termination of the Classic, at least in Middle America, produced the greatest shock. Acceptance of the radiocarbon dates requires acceptance of the Spinden correlation, and this creates a gap between A.D. 650 and 900. Such an interval can be filled by drastic rearrangement of existing ideas. It would be necessary to believe that the final centuries of the Maya civilization witnessed a prolonged and drab decline. Otherwise it is necessary to assume that a cultural horizon, the Tula-Toltec, persisted for some 400 years, twice as long as previously believed. This latter also requires a compensating drop back in time of the late post-Classic cultures. The dilemma in Peru is quite similar, except that there is no indigenous system of dating, and it is not so difficult to stretch out the Classic to cover the long span of years from late B.C. times to about A.D. 1000. This latter is the usual estimate for the beginning of the Tiahuanaco horizon.

These considerations form a basis for concluding, even in the face of controversy, that the results of the radiocarbon dating method are, in general, sound. The examination and comparison of several sequences in Middle and South America serve to segregate dates on samples which are unsatisfactory or wrong and to indicate incompatibilities between some sequences. Importantly, however, the dates have contributed to ideas concerning the chronology of culture development in a large part of the New World. In some cases adjustments of archeological ideas to correspond with time determinations by radiocarbon require no drastic modification. Otherwise, as in the question of the age of the Classic cultures, particularly the Maya, necessary adjustments can be made, but they are far from satisfactory to an impressive body of scholars. In view of the really small number of dates and the character of some of the samples from this Classic period, one can only record that full agreement between archeology and radiocarbon results is not possible. Without much question a clarification of this incompatibility involving the Classic cultures of America is one of the most urgent matters requiring the attention of both archeologists and physicists. Examination of some above-mentioned dates which are obviously wrong gives rise to questions concerning the assignment of the samples to specific strata. As an example, one chooses, for Classic Mochica of the north coast of Peru, the date A.D. 112 ± 190 (No. C-619), which came from a late Mochica burial with clearly identifiable pottery. Another date, 873 ± 500 B.C. (No. C-382), is discarded, at least as a Mochica date, for it is much too early. The latter sample is described as ash mixed with bone. It was located on the habitation site, ground level, beneath the pyramid Huaca del Sol at Moche, a pyramid considered to be Mochica. This location is rather difficult to assign precisiley, and, in view of the date and its conflict with the Formative, one can hazard a guess that, owing to difficulties of collection, the sample does not correspond to its description. In contrast to the preceding there are a few dates from the region which are not correct, but the source of the error cannot be determined from available records. A type of question also arises in considering data such as the earliest date at Bat Cave. The date 3981 ± 310 B.C. (No. C-573) was determined on charcoal from a lower level in the cave. Whether or not this actually dates the occurrence of maize is not certain, for a full account of the excavation has not yet been published. On the basis of other data it has been guessed that the date on corn will be about 2500 B.C. These figures are most tenuous; possibly they should not be published. Another error is an example of probable curatorial problems. The date 1475 ± 230 (No. C-423) for Teotihuacán III is obviously wrong, and one needs only to read that the sample was collected in 1921 in order to assume that it has become contaminated in some fashion.

The evaluation employed for the Middle and South American material could be expanded if space permitted. Sequences of dates on strata in southwestern North America and on samples from caves and other deposits in the Great Basin and the West Coast region provide a chronological framework, particularly for the "early Lithic" and "Archaic" cultures.[11] Here we see, for example, a sequence of dates on the stages of the Cochise culture of Arizona (Nos. C-511, C-515, C-518, C-519, and C-556). These ages are now generally accepted and appear to be compatible with most geological opinion as well as with contributing archeological evidence. Similarly dates from Nevada, Oregon, and California indicate that man was well established in the region previous to 7000 B.C. This series of radiocarbon dates has contributed to the steadily growing opinion that cultures other than those of the Folsom-Yuma tradition were contemporaneous with it. One reads also of the opinion that Folsom may have developed in the region east of the Rocky Mountains to move northward during the latter part of its existence.

Dates on eastern archeological complexes are as yet far too few to permit any general regional interpretations. The initial attempts to date Adena and Hopewell cultures and some phases of the Archaic cultures in the Southeast were far from satisfactory, largely because many of the samples were unsuitable for this purpose. Determinations since 1952 confirm the general opinion that Adena preceded Hopewell. In addition, the dates indicate that the two cultures overlapped in time. Many more dates are needed, and additional archeological analysis such as that recently published by Fowler[12] must be completed before this problem, one of many in the East, may be solved.

Of specific interest are two dates on the "Old Copper" culture apparently centered in Wisconsin. Three samples produced two dates, 3650 ± 600 years (No. C-836) and 5560 ± 600 years (Nos. C-837 and C-839). The full significance of these dates is uncertain at this writing. The culture has long been recognized as an old one. The indicated ages are, however, a little surprising. It is possibly not significant to comment that these are the earliest dates known for a copper industry, at least in the New World.

The significance to archeology of eight dates from Barbeau Creek Rock Shelter (Nos. C-899, C-900, C-903, C-904, C-905, C-907, and C-908) is not known, for a report on the excavation has not

11. Willey and Phillips, n.d.   12. Fowler, 1955.

been issued. However, the dates from the lowest levels, ranging from about 7100 B.C. to 8600 B.C., are the earliest recorded for the presence of man in the East. Some of these are obviously of the order of "early Lithic" dates, but the culture may be classifiable as Archaic. The site "consists of a 25.5-foot-deep midden deposit and is situated at the base of an 82-foot sandstone bluff that projects over and protects the site" (cf. p. 101 above). The method of collecting the samples by "hand picking," washing in water, screening, and so on, as described in the listing of the dates, should be of particular interest to collectors. There is considerable variation in some of the dates, but it is not possible to assess the significance of these, and we await with interest the analysis and conclusions of the excavators of the site.

The situation in regard to dates on geological events is analogous to that in archeology. That is, there exists, particularly for North America, a basic but incomplete chronological framework to which additions are being constantly made. In this, there are dates which are either obviously wrong or subject to controversy. There are geologists, too, who seriously question the validity of some sequences of dates. As far as it is possible for a student outside the field to judge, the reasons for these difficulties are quite similar to those mentioned for archeology. Aside from contaminated samples, the reason for which may or may not be discoverable, the major source of disagreement can be traced to the process of selection and collection of samples. It does appear that a large proportion of the controversy concerning accuracy of dates or sequences of them is based actually upon disagreement concerning interpretation of the stratigraphy. The foregoing statement does not suggest or imply in any way adverse criticism, for such would be most unrealistic, if not illogical. At the present stage of geological knowledge there are numerous stratigraphic situations which are open to varying interpretation. However, it may be suggested that, given a truly representative sample, or preferably a series of them from a stratigraphic sequence, the radiocarbon dates can be of major assistance in determining the order and timing of geological events. In order to do this, however, it is sometimes necessary to revise a number of deeply intrenched and unprovable opinions concerning time required by geological processes, such as the advance and retreat of glacial ice.

Of all phenomena which have been dated by radiocarbon, the age of the Two Creeks Forest Bed in Wisconsin is the most certain. At least seven concordant determinations have been made by two laboratories (Nos. C-380, C-365, C-366, C-536, C-537, W-42, and W-83).[13] The age of the forest bed averages about 11,400 ± 350 years (9400 B.C.). This and a number of other dates, for example, Nos. C-674 and C-630, establishes the maximum of the Mankato advance of the Wisconsin ice at about 10,000 years ago. It is possible to correlate a number of succeeding dates with various stages of development of the Great Lakes and propose, as Flint has done, a very tentative but nonetheless important and interesting account of late Wisconsin substage and events in the northeastern United States and southeastern Canada.[14] In spite of uncertainties concerning some details, there is considerable background supporting the major contentions. Although these are promising as far as geology in the East and within the boundary of the glaciated area is concerned, correlations with deposits and other phenomena in unglaciated regions poses a number of complicated problems which have not been solved at this writing. The dates in Danger Cave, Utah (Nos. C-609, C-610, C-611, C-635, C-636, and C-640), challenge some previous correlations and inferred chronologies of the various shorelines established during the history of Lake Bonneville. By implication, this also involved interpretations of the significance of moraines and analogous deposits in the Rocky Mountains. These are major problems which are the subject of continuing research.

Another series of dates contributing to closely related problems has been published since 1952. The progress of the development of the gas counting method has made possible the refinement of dates which were somewhat beyond the reach of the solid-carbon method employed by Libby. Combined with these remeasurements, additional dates on older materials begin to point to possible correlations of Tazewell, Cary, and earlier stages of the Wisconsin Age. The chronology of pre-Mankato advance and retreat of glacial ice across Pennsylvania, Ohio, Illinois, Indiana, and Iowa can be outlined.[15] There is some disagreement as to how the dates should be

13. Suess, 1954.   14. Flint, 1953.

15. Andover Conference on Radiocarbon Dating. Discussions of presentations by Flint and Horberg served to outline several points of view.

labeled and which ones are incompatible, but nevertheless a reasonable scheme can be postulated. Comparison of these dates with the dates from layers in Searles Lake (Nos. C-894, C-895, C-896, and C-897) supports the suspicion that dates in the East are of the correct magnitude and that various phenomena outside the glaciated region may be correlated with them. Such an idea is subject to controversy, to say the least.[16] The series of interlocking problems are the subject of several investigations being carried out by R. F. Flint in collaboration with M. Rubin, W. A. Gale, and others.[17]

The preceding discussions have been based entirely upon information from the New World, largely because the greatest number of age determinations are from this hemisphere. A glance at the measurements from the Old World reveals the fact that the status of the method is closely parallel to that in the Americas. There are dates of unquestioned validity; there are dates which present problems in interpretation; and there are dates which undoubtedly are wrong for reasons which have already been explained.

One series of dates is of great interest. The age of the Alleröd period in Europe established initially by Libby's measurements, and especially as a result of research by the Carbon-14 Dating Laboratory at Copenhagen,[18] has proved that the Alleröd in Europe was contemporaneous with the Two Creeks Forest Bed in Wisconsin. This suggests the probability that Pleistocene events in the Old World and the New World were synchronous. Additional but less certain evidence of contemporaneity of events may be inferred from the date from Poggenwisch, Holstein, Germany. The age is 15,150 ± 350 years (No. W-93),[19] and it is a date for an Upper Paleolithic reindeer-hunting culture. Also it belongs in the "Older Dryas" level according to pollen analysts. The sample was associated with the drift of the Pomeranian glacier, which may, by collation of other sequential information, be tentatively correlated with the Cary glaciation in North America.

The various dates from the Near East are of equal interest. Those from samples of known age have been mentioned. Samples from

16. See, e.g., Antevs, 1953, 1954.

17. Personal communication, January, 1955.

18. Flint and Deevey, 1951, p. 266; Anderson *et al.*, 1953; Iverson, 1953.

19. Suess, 1954.

Nippur (No. C-752) were used to test the limit of sensitivity of the method. As a result of 1 month of steady counting time for each of three samples the date 1993 ± 106 B.C. strongly favors the younger of the possible calendars derived from the Mesopotamian king lists. This date serves to fix a point in "the whole interwoven fabric of historic interrelationships of western Asia and Egypt in the early part of the second millennium B.C." Other dates from the Near East of interest and importance are the dates on the early Neolithic site at Jarmo in Iraq (Nos. C-113, C-742, C-743, and C-744). The dates from the lower levels indicate the general age of the beginning of village life at a preceramic stage of culture development in the Fertile Crescent.

To terminate here comments on the radiocarbon dates which have been published is to provide an account having significant lacunae. Much has been omitted concerning the Old World, but it is expected that the development of laboratories now progressing in Cambridge and London, Copenhagen, Göteborg, Heidelberg, Rome, Stockholm, and Trondheim will result in reports and discussions which will fill the gap. Also, little has been said specifically concerning the relationship between some dates and pollen chronology. This has been the subject of some valuable comments,[20] and, of course, some of the discussion of geological problems includes by implication information from pollen analysis from both the Old World and the New. Also omitted have been comments on oceanographic problems,[21] for these are far beyond the competence of the present author. It is to be hoped that these omissions are not serious, since a study of world-wide radiocarbon chronology was not the purpose of this essay. The intent was to indicate the scope of the method and its general usefulness as a tool to be employed by any field which was concerned with appropriate subject matter. Dates and sequences in American archeology and geology were briefly listed and discussed as examples of the usefulness of a method having the attributes of the one under consideration. Because of the recency of the method, cogitation over the validity of the results was inevitably a subject of much of the discussion. It is our contention that the magnitude of the error inherent in the

20. Deevey and Potzger, 1951; Flint and Deevey, 1951.

21. Kulp, 1952, has a short outline of the problems in oceanography at that time.

method is not so large as the number of years quoted for the purpose of invalidating it. It is also our opinion that, barring mistakes by collectors and laboratory workers, the very large majority of the errors are traceable to the process of selection and collection of samples. Such range all the way from faulty observation of conditions in the ground to controversy over the significance of a given stratum. More than anything else the record of success is ample proof that the superlative research of Libby and his associates have provided science with a valuable and uniquely useful tool.

BIBLIOGRAPHY

ANDERSON, E. C., LEVI, HILDE, and TAUBER, H. 1953. "Copenhagen Natural Radiocarbon Measurements I," *Science*, **118**, 4–6.

ANDOVER CONFERENCE ON RADIOCARBON DATING, OCTOBER 21–23, 1954, PHILLIPS ACADEMY, ANDOVER, MASSACHUSETTS. An unpublished stenographic record of the discussions.

ANTEVS, ERNST. 1953. "Geochronology of the Deglacial and Neothermal Ages," *J. Geol.*, **61**, 195–230.

———. 1954. "Geochronology of the Deglacial and Neothermal Ages: A Reply," *ibid.*, **62**, 516–21.

BIRD, JUNIUS. 1951. "South American Radiocarbon Dates," in FREDERICK JOHNSON (ed.), *Radiocarbon Dating: A Report on the Program to Aid in Development of the Method of Dating* ("Society for American Archaeology Memoirs," No. 8 [Salt Lake City, 1951]), pp. 37–49.

DEEVEY, EDWARD S., JR., and POTZGER, JOHN E. 1951. "Peat Samples for Radiocarbon Analysis: Problems in Pollen Statistics," *Am. J. Sci.*, **249**, 473–511.

DEEVEY, EDWARD S., JR., GROSS, MARSHA S., HUTCHINSON, G. E., and KRAYBILL, HENRY L. 1954. "The Natural C-14 Contents of Materials from Hard-Water Lakes," *Proc. Nat. Acad. Sci.*, **40**, 285–88.

FLINT, RICHARD FOSTER. 1953. "Probable Wisconsin Substages and Late-Wisconsin Events in Northeastern United States and Southeastern Canada," *Bull. Geol. Soc. Am.*, **64**, 897–919.

FLINT, RICHARD FOSTER, and DEEVEY, EDWARD S., JR. 1951. "Radiocarbon Dating of Late-Pleistocene Events," *Am. J. Sci.*, **249**, 257–300.

FOWLER, MELVIN L. 1955. "Ware Grouping and Decorations of Woodland Ceramics in Illinois," *Am. Antiquity*, **20**, 213–25.

GRIFFIN, JAMES B. 1952. "Radiocarbon Dates for the Eastern United States," in JAMES B. GRIFFIN (ed.), *Archaeology of the Eastern United States* (Chicago, 1952), pp. 365–70. (This chapter lists, among others, a number of dates determined by the University of Michigan Memorial–Phoenix Project Radiocarbon Laboratory.)

HOPKINS, B. M., and GIDDINGS, J. L., JR. 1953. *Geological Background of the Iyatayet Archaeological Site, Cape Denbigh, Alaska.* ("Smithsonian Miscellaneous Collections," Vol. **121**, No. 11.) Washington, D.C.

IVERSON, JOHS. 1953. "Radiocarbon Dating of the Alleröd Period," *Science*, **118**, 4–11.

JOHNSON, FREDERICK (ed.). 1951. *Radiocarbon Dating: A Report on the Program To Aid in Development of the Method of Dating.* ("Society for American Archaeology Memoirs," No. 8.) Salt Lake City.

KULP, J. LAURENCE. 1952. "The Carbon-14 Method of Age Determination," *Scientific Monthly*, **75**, 259–67.

KULP, J. LAURENCE, FEELEY, HERBERT W., and TRYON, LANSING E. 1951. "Lamont Natural Radiocarbon Measurements I," *Science*, **114**, 565–68.

KULP, J. LAURENCE, TRYON, LANSING E., ECKELMAN, WALTER R., and SNAIL, WILLIAM A. 1952. "Lamont Natural Radiocarbon Measurements II." *Science*, **116**, 409–14.

RALPH, ELIZABETH. 1955. "University of Pennsylvania Radiocarbon Dates I," *Science*, **121**, 149–51.

SUESS, HANS E. 1954. "U.S. Geological Survey Radiocarbon Dates I," *Science*, **120**, 467–73.

WILLEY, GORDON R. 1954. "Archaeological Problems and Radiocarbon Dates in South and Middle America." (Manuscript of paper presented to the Andover Conference on Radiocarbon Dating, October 21–23, 1954.)

WILLEY, GORDON R., and PHILLIPS, PHILIP. n.d. "Methods and Theory in American Archaeology. II. Historical Developmental Interpretation." (Manuscript.)

APPENDIX A

SPECIAL EQUIPMENT AND CHEMICALS FOR THE C^{14} SAMPLE PREPARATION APPARATUS

Item	Source
Vycor combustion tubes; 25 mm. I.D., 31 mm. O.D., 750 mm.	Corning Glass Works
Iron tube; 30 inches, $1\frac{1}{4}$ O.D., 0.035 wall	Central Steel and Wire Company
Copper oxide; wire form	Merck and Company
Hydrochloric acid, CP	Baker and Adamson Company
Ammonia CP	Baker and Adamson Company
Calcium chloride, dihydrate, AR	Mallinckrodt Chemical Company
Magnesium turnings, CP	Merck and Company
Cadmium metal	*See* Dr. Bergman (Institute for the Study of Metals)
Furnace tubes, alumdum; 4 cm. I.D., 9-inch lengths or longer	Norton Company
Nichrome wire, Nos. 20 and 28	Driver-Harris Company
Pyrex fritted disks; medium; No. 39570-10	Sargent Company
Drierite; mesh No. 4	Sargent Company

APPENDIX B

SPECIAL MATERIALS FOR SCREEN-WALL COUNTER

Item	Source	Type
Unleaded brass tubing (direct from mill, $51.70 per 100 lb.)	American Brass, 1327 West Washington Street, Chicago, Illinois (Mr. Baker)	
Stainless Steel	Steel Sales	18-8; Type 304, 302
Copper (Commercial Copper)	Chas. Besley, Chicago	
Spool copper-clad iron-core wire, Nos. 28 (0.012) and 30	Sylvania Electric Company	

INDEXES

INDEX OF SUBJECTS

INDEX OF NAMES

INDEX OF SAMPLES

PHOENIX BOOKS
in Science

PHOENIX SCIENCE SERIES

PHOENIX BOOKS
Sociology, Anthropology, and Archeology